istics and

ations of

Semiconductor Electronics Education Committee Books

Characteristics and Limitations of Transistors

Semiconductor Electronics Education Committee, Volume 4

Richard D. Thornton
Massachusetts Institute of Technology

David DeWitt
International Business Machines Corp.

Paul E. Gray
Massachusetts Institute of Technology

E. R. Chenette
University of Minnesota

NEW ENGLAND INSTITUTE
OF TECHNOLOGY
LEARNING RESOURCES CENTER

John Wiley & Sons, Inc., New York · London · Sydney

568748

11-89

Foreword

The importance of transistors and other semiconductor devices is now well established. The subsequent development of micro-miniaturized electronic circuits has blurred the dividing line between the "device" and the "circuit," and thus has made it increasingly important for us to understand deeply the relationship between the internal physics and structure of a device, and its potentialities for circuit performance. Furthermore, the small size and efficient operation of semiconductor devices make possible for the first time a much closer integration between the theoretical and laboratory aspects of the educational process.

To prepare new educational material which would reflect these developments, there was formed in the Fall of 1960 a group known as the Semiconductor Electronics Education Committee (SEEC). This committee is comprised of university and industrial members, brought together by several of the faculty of the Electrical Engineering Department at the Massachusetts Institute of Technology, with Professor C. L. Searle acting as Chairman and Professor R. B. Adler acting as Technical Director. The committee undertook the production of a multipurpose course in semiconductor electronics, designed primarily for use in universities at the third or fourth year undergraduate level.

The success of the high-school physics course developed by the Physical Science Study Committee (PSSC) led the SEEC to believe that the same kind of combination used there—text, laboratory experiments, and films, in a complementary format—would be the most practical way of providing uniformly high-quality instruction over the wide range of material involved. It was hoped that this arrangement would lead to broad applicability of the course in the academic world, and also in some professional training activities of industry and government. This book is one in the SEEC series, all volumes of which are listed here:*

Vol. 1 (ISP)   *Introduction to Semiconductor Physics,* R. B. Adler, A. C. Smith, and R. L. Longini

Vol. 2 (PEM)   *Physical Electronics and Circuit Models of Transistors,* P. E. Gray, D. DeWitt, A. R. Boothroyd, and J. F. Gibbons

Vol. 3 (ECP)   *Elementary Circuit Properties of Transistors,* C. L. Searle, A. R. Boothroyd, E. J. Angelo, Jr., P. E. Gray, and D. O. Pederson

Vol. 4 (CLT)   *Characteristics and Limitations of Transistors,* R. D. Thornton, D. DeWitt, P. E. Gray, and E. R. Chenette

Vol. 5 (MTC)   *Multistage Transistor Circuits,* R. D. Thornton, C. L. Searle, D. O. Pederson, R. B. Adler, and E. J. Angelo, Jr.

Vol. 6 (DTC)   *Digital Transistor Circuits,* J. N. Harris and P. E. Gray

Vol. 7 (TCM)   *Handbook of Basic Transistor Circuits and Measurements,* R. D. Thornton, J. G. Linvill, E. R. Chenette, H. L. Ablin, J. N. Harris, A. R. Boothroyd, and J. Willis

These books have all gone through at least one "preliminary edition," many through two or more. The preliminary editions were used in teaching trials at some of the participating colleges and industrial training activities, and the results have been used as a basis for revision.

* Minor changes in title or authorship may take place in some of the volumes, which are still in preparation at the time of this writing.

It is almost impossible to enumerate all those people who have contributed some of their effort to the SEEC. Certain ones, however, have either been active with the Committee steadily since its inception, or have made very major contributions since then. These may be thought of as "charter members," deserving special mention.

From Universities

California, Berkeley: D. O. Pederson
Imperial College London: A. R. Boothroyd△
Iowa State: H. L. Ablin*
M.I.T.: R. B. Adler, P. E. Gray, A. L. McWhorter, C. L. Searle,
     A. C. Smith, R. D. Thornton, J. R. Zacharias, H. J.
     Zimmermann (Research Laboratory of Electronics),
     J. N. Harris (Lincoln Laboratory)
Minnesota: E. R. Chenette
New Mexico: W. W. Grannemann
Polytechnic Institute of Brooklyn: E. J. Angelo, Jr.
Stanford: J. F. Gibbons, J. G. Linvill
U.C.L.A.: J. Willis

From Industries

Bell Telephone Laboratories: J. M. Early, A. N. Holden, V. R.
     Saari
Fairchild Semiconductor: V. R. Grinich
IBM: D. DeWitt
RCA: J. Hilibrand, E. O. Johnson, J. I. Pankove
Transitron: B. Dale,† H. G. Rudenberg‡
Westinghouse Research Laboratories: A. I. Bennett, H. C. Lin,
     R. L. Longini§

General management of the SEEC operations is in the hands of Educational Services, Inc. (abbreviated ESI), Watertown, Mass.,

△ Now at Queen's University, Belfast.
* Now at the University of Nebraska, Department of Electrical Engineering.
† Now at Sylvania Corp.
‡ Now at A. D. Little, Inc.
§ Now at Carnegie Institute of Technology, Department of Electrical Engineering.

a nonprofit corporation that grew out of the PSSC activities and is presently engaged in a number of educational projects at various levels. In addition to providing general management, ESI has supplied all the facilities necessary for preparing the SEEC films. These are 16-mm sound films, 30 to 40 minutes in length, designed to supplement the subject matter and laboratory experiments presented in the various text books. The film titles are:

"Gap Energy and Recombination Light in Germanium"— J. I. Pankove and R. B. Adler

"Minority Carriers in Semiconductors"—J. R. Haynes and W. Shockley

"Transistor Structure and Technology"—J. M. Early and R. D. Thornton

Pending arrangements for commercial distribution, these films are available (purchase or rental) directly from Educational Services, Inc., 47 Galen Street, Watertown, Mass.

The committee has also endeavored to develop laboratory materials for use with the books and films. This material is referred to in the books and further information about it can be obtained from ESI.

The preparation of the entire SEEC program, including all the books, was supported at first under a general grant made to the Massachusetts Institute of Technology by the Ford Foundation, for the purpose of aiding in the improvement of engineering education, and subsequently by specific grants made to ESI by the National Science Foundation. This support is gratefully acknowledged.

Campbell L. Searle
Chairman, SEEC
Richard B. Adler
Technical Director, SEEC

Preface

This book is concerned with characteristics and limitations of *real* transistors. The reader is assumed to be familiar with both the first-order, idealized physical theory of transistor operation and its relation to circuit models and simple circuits. The purpose of this volume is to examine other important physical processes, particularly those which limit the allowable range of voltage, current, temperature, and speed of response of actual transistors. In some cases the important results are expressed as modifications of the simple models, while in other cases special circuit analysis techniques are developed. The objective has been to concentrate attention on those transistor limitations which cannot be circumvented by the cleverest of circuit designs.

It is possible to design transistor circuits without a knowledge of most of the material in this book. When a design problem is simple and component cost not important, we can achieve acceptable results with only a modest understanding of the transistor. If, however, we are concerned with minimizing cost, improving reliability, or if we are attempting to advance the state-of-the-art of *either* circuit design *or* device design, then a knowledge of the material in this book is vital. In these areas we must be thoroughly familiar with the second-order properties of the transistors because those properties usually produce *first-order* design problems. To use a simple analogy, the problem of designing a bridge is seldom one of achieving the correct length. The difficulties are more likely to be associated with thermal expansion, wind loading, freezing, etc. Likewise, with state-of-the-art circuit design the obvious problems are solved first, and often the most difficult problems are not anticipated in advance and usually cannot be solved by recourse to the simple model of a transistor.

This book should be usable by anyone with a knowledge of elementary electronic circuits (for example, dependent generators, RLC circuits, ideal diodes, load lines, etc.) and an understanding of the physical origin of the parameters in the hybrid-π and Ebers-Moll transistor circuit models. In particular, it assumes a knowledge of most of the material in the first three volumes of the SEEC series as listed in the Foreword.

The principle writing staff of this volume is indebted to the entire SEEC membership for ideas and criticisms which have led to major improvements in this book. Credit is particularly due to Professors R. B. Adler and C. L. Searle of M.I.T. and Dr. J. M. Early of Bell Telephone Laboratories.

R. D. THORNTON
D. DeWITT
P. E. GRAY
E. R. CHENETTE

Cambridge, Mass.
February 1966

Contents

Characteristics and
Limitations of
Transistors

1

Transistor Performance at Extremes
of Current and Voltage

1.0 INTRODUCTION

Several circuit models are commonly used to represent the first-order electrical behavior of transistors. The hybrid-π linear incremental circuit model shown in Fig. 1.1a is one such description. Another is the charge-control model which describes the nonlinear dynamic behavior of the transistor, and which reduces to the Ebers-Moll two-diode model of Fig. 1.1b under dc steady-state conditions.*

The incremental-gain mechanism of the transistor is represented in the hybrid-π model by the dependent current generator. Under low-level injection conditions, the *transconductance* g_m is

$$g_m = \frac{q|I_C|}{kT} \tag{1.1}$$

---

* The reader is assumed to be familiar with these models, with their use in circuits, and with the physical electronics on which they are based. Three other books in this series deal with appropriate material. These are: R. B. Adler, A. C. Smith, and R. L. Longini, *Introduction to Semiconductor Physics;* P. E. Gray, D. DeWitt, A. R. Boothroyd, and J. F. Gibbons, *Physical Electronics and Circuit Models of Transistors;* and C. L. Searle, A. R. Boothroyd, E. J. Angelo, Jr., P. E. Gray, and D. O. Pederson, *Elementary Circuit Properties of Transistors,* hereafter referred to as ISP, PEM, and ECP, respectively.

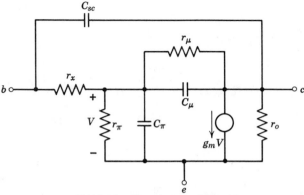

(a) Hybrid-π linear incremental model

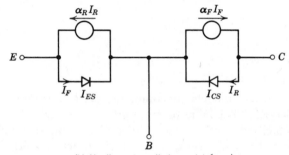

(b) Nonlinear two-diode model *(pnp)*

Fig. 1.1. First-order circuit models for transistors.

where I_C is the dc collector current at the operating point, and kT/q is the *thermal voltage* (25 mv at $T = 290°K$). The resistance r_π accounts for the recombination of minority carriers in the base and in the emitter. It is related to the low-frequency common-emitter short-circuit incremental current gain β_0 in the following manner:

$$g_m r_\pi = \beta_0$$

The capacitance C_π represents the effects of space-charge capacitance at the emitter junction, as well as the storage of excess carriers in the base and emitter regions. That is,

$$C_\pi = C_b + C_{je}$$

where C_b denotes the base (and emitter)-charging capacitance and C_{je} is the emitter space-charge capacitance.

The capacitance C_μ represents, principally, the space-charge capacitance of the collector junction.

The output resistance r_o, the feedback resistance r_μ, and a small component of C_μ represent the effects of *base-width modulation* caused by the dependence on collector-base voltage of the width of the portion of the collector space-charge layer on the base side. These base-width modulation effects become important only when the voltage gain of the transistor is large, that is, when variations in collector-base voltage are much greater than variations in emitter-base voltage.

The *base resistance* r_x and the separation of the collector space-charge capacitance into C_μ and C_{sc} are the first-order consequences of transverse voltage drops in the base region.*

The Ebers-Moll model of Fig. 1.1b is characterized by two junction saturation currents, I_{ES} and I_{CS}, and two short-circuit current gains α_F and α_R. This model has been derived for an idealized transistor in which low-level injection is assumed, base-width modulation is neglected, and the effects of transverse voltage drops in the base are ignored.

Both first-order circuit models shown in Fig. 1.1 are based upon several assumptions which relate to the physical electronics of transistors. These assumptions are given below.

(1) Steady-state junction currents result solely from the injection or extraction of minority carriers in the quasi-neutral semiconductor volume. Currents associated with the generation or recombination of carriers in the space-charge layers or on the surface are neglected, as are currents resulting from the multiplication of carriers in the space-charge layer by the avalanche mechanism.

(2) The concentrations of injected minority carriers are small enough so that the majority-carrier concentrations remain essentially equal to their equilibrium values. That is, *low-level injection* is assumed.

---

* Variations in voltage, concentration, and current density on planes parallel to the junctions are referred to as *transverse*. Variations normal to the junction planes are described as *longitudinal*. Components of current density are denoted similarly.

(3) The physical effect of the *transverse* voltage drops in the base region upon the *longitudinal* flow of minority carriers is neglected.

Because of these assumptions, the first-order analysis does not explain the limits on current and voltage which exist for all transistors. Nor does it account for some of the significant variations in electrical parameters which occur even before the maximum values of current and voltage are reached. These factors frequently limit the performance of a transistor in a particular application, and often increase the complexity of the task faced by the circuit designer. Therefore, it is important to understand their origins in terms of physical electronics and their consequences in terms of circuit behavior.

In this chapter we explore phenomena which cause the behavior of transistors to deviate from that described by the first-order models of Fig. 1.1, and determine the effects of these physical mechanisms on the electrical parameters which are used to describe the circuit performance of transistors. In addition, we investigate the physical mechanisms which require the establishment of current and voltage limits.*

At very *low levels* of dc collector current, the currents associated with recombination in the emitter-junction space-charge layer and on its surfaces become comparable to the currents associated with recombination in the neutral regions of the transistor. The effect of these surface and space-charge-layer recombination currents upon the incremental current gain is considered in Sec. 1.1.

Several physical mechanisms, listed below, influence the performance of transistors at *high levels* of current or voltage.

(1) At moderate-to-high levels of collector current the store of minority carriers in the base region becomes large enough so that the majority-carrier concentration increases significantly above its equilibrium value throughout much of the base region. In Sec. 1.2 we explore the consequences of this *high-level* injection situation.

---

* We exclude from this discussion limitations on current and voltage which are imposed by the thermal considerations that relate to internal power dissipation. Power and temperature limitations are considered in Chapter 2.

(2) As the base current of a transistor increases to high levels, transverse ohmic voltage drops appear in the base region. The effects of these drops are considered in Sec. 1.3.

(3) At high levels of collector current, longitudinal ohmic voltage drops in the collector region may influence the switching characteristics of a transistor significantly. These voltage drops are discussed in Sec. 1.4.

(4) The effective width of the base region of a transistor varies in response to changes in the widths of the junction space-charge layers. Consequently, as we shall see in Sec. 1.5, high levels of collector current or of collector-base voltage cause significant changes in the base width.

(5) At high levels of the junction voltages, avalanche multiplication in the space-charge layers contributes to the terminal currents. We explore the consequences of carrier multiplication in Sec. 1.6.

Because these second-order effects are nonlinear in nature, their simultaneous presence may not produce behavior which is, in any sense, equivalent to the superposition of the individual contributions. Furthermore, simultaneous analytical treatment of these second-order effects leads to very complex results of limited utility. Therefore, we establish the nature and characteristics of these second-order effects *separately* at the level of the physical electronics. Since the electrical parameters of the incremental model for a transistor may be influenced by several of the second-order physical mechanisms, we postpone a thorough discussion of the high-level behavior of the model parameters and of the relative significance of the physical effects at various levels of current and voltage until Sec. 1.7, after the physical effects have been investigated.

Finally, the current and voltage ratings of a transistor are considered in Sec. 1.8.

1.1 INCREMENTAL CURRENT GAIN AT LOW LEVELS OF COLLECTOR CURRENT

According to the idealized first-order model, the incremental current gain β_0 is independent of the dc collector current. The current gain of the model is constant because all recombination is

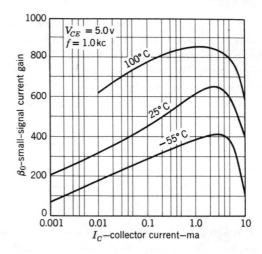

Fig. 1.2. β_0 versus I_C for a 2N3117 silicon transistor.

assumed to occur in the bulk, and the bulk lifetime is constant. Most silicon transistors have values of β_0 which *decrease* as the collector current decreases, as illustrated in Fig. 1.2. That is, the incremental base current of these transistors is *larger* for small values of bias current than is predicted by the idealized model, in which base current increments result solely from changes in recombination in the neutral base and emitter regions. The extra incremental base current, which causes the decrease in β_0 shown in Fig. 1.2 at low bias currents, results from the recombination of excess carriers on the surfaces and in the emitter space-charge layer.

These surface and space-charge layer recombination components of the incremental base current are seen only at low collector currents because they are less strongly dependent on the emitter bias voltage V_{EB} than is the bulk recombination current. We can illustrate the differences in voltage dependence by considering the nonequilibrium carrier concentrations in the space-charge layer. The hole concentration, for example, varies from approximately p_{po} at the p-type edge of the space charge layer to $p_{po}e^{-q(\psi_0 - V_{EB})/kT}$ at the n-type edge* (the contact potential is denoted by ψ_0). The

---

* PEM, Sec. 2.3.3; we consider a *pnp* transistor for which positive values of V_{EB} correspond to forward bias.

minority-carrier hole concentration at the edge of the n-type region can also be written as $p_{no}e^{qV_{EB}/kT}$, inasmuch as the equilibrium minority-carrier concentration p_{no} is related to the contact potential by

$$p_{no} = p_{po}e^{-q\psi_0/kT}$$

The rate of recombination in the neutral base region, which is, of course, proportional to the excess minority-carrier concentration, thus varies as $p_{no}(e^{qV_{EB}/kT} - 1)$, and the corresponding *incremental* component of recombination current varies with operating point as $p_{no}e^{qV_{EB}/kT}$.

The recombination rate *within* the space-charge layer clearly varies from point to point because the hole and electron concentrations vary from one edge of the space-charge layer to the other. We consider an *average* rate of recombination in the space-charge layer (and on its surface) which is proportional to either the hole or electron concentration at the plane in the space-charge layer where the electrostatic potential is halfway between the values at the edges.* At this plane the hole concentration is approximately:

$$p_{po}e^{-q(\psi_0 - V_{EB})/2kT} = p_{po}\sqrt{\frac{p_{no}}{p_{po}}}e^{qV_{EB}/2kT}$$

The corresponding recombination rate is thus proportional to $\sqrt{p_{no}}e^{qV_{EB}/2kT}$. Consequently, at large values of V_{EB} (and thus of I_C), the surface and space-charge-layer recombination components of the incremental base current, which vary approximately as $\sqrt{p_{no}}e^{qV_{EB}/2kT}$, are masked by the bulk recombination current, which varies as $p_{no}e^{qV_{EB}/kT}$.

The decrease in β_0 which occurs at low levels of I_C is more apparent in silicon than in germanium transistors. This fact arises from another feature of the results discussed above. For fixed V_{EB}, the bulk recombination components of the incremental base current are proportional to the equilibrium minority-carrier concentration p_{no}, which is, in turn, proportional to the square of the intrinsic carrier concentration, $n_i{}^2$, whereas the surface and space-

---

* The consequences of this assumption of an average recombination rate are supported by detailed analysis of the space-charge layer. See, for example, Ref. 1.1.

charge-layer components are proportional to $\sqrt{p_{no}}$, or to n_i. Therefore, the ratio of the bulk component to the surface and space-charge-layer components is proportional to n_i. Near room temperature, n_i is about three orders of magnitude greater for germanium than for silicon,* so that only the bulk component is seen in germanium transistors at typical values of V_{EB}. The surface and space-charge layer components can be placed in evidence in a germanium transistor by operating it at greatly reduced temperatures (less than about $200°\mathrm{K}$), thereby suppressing n_i, or by operating at unusually low values of V_{EB}.† At such low temperatures or abnormally low voltages, β_0 decreases with current at low values of quiescent current, in the same manner shown in Fig. 1.2.‡

The data of Fig. 1.2 show that the recombination rate in *all* portions of the base and in the emitter space-charge layer decreases with increasing temperature, thereby increasing β_0 as discussed in ECP, Sec. 4.3.

1.2 HIGH-LEVEL INJECTION IN THE BASE REGION

The distribution of excess minority-carrier charge in the base is approximately triangular in shape for operation in the normal region, as shown in Fig. 1.3a (drawn for a *pnp* transistor). At the emitter edge of the neutral base region ($x = 0$) the minority-carrier concentration $p_b(0)$ is increased above the equilibrium value p_{bo} as a consequence of the forward bias on the emitter junction. At the collector edge ($x = W$), the minority-carrier concentration is negligible in comparison with p_{bo} because of the reverse bias on the collector junction.

---

* See, for example, ISP, Sec. 1.5.4.

† Germanium transistors are seldom operated at values of V_{EB} small enough to make the effects of space-charge-layer currents apparent at room temperature, because the corresponding quiescent collector current would be dominated by the collector-junction saturation current, which is thermally generated. For this same reason it is necessary to express the dependence of β_0 in terms of I_E rather than I_C, because I_C is sensibly independent of V_{EB} for small values of V_{EB}.

‡ As noted in ECP, Ch. 4, in some germanium transistors, β_0 falls off at low currents because of surface leakage currents which shunt the emitter-base junction. These leakage currents depend on V_{EB} more or less linearly, and thus become important only at very small quiescent currents.

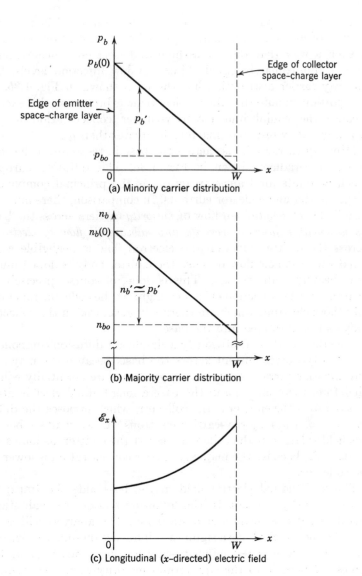

Fig. 1.3. Carrier distributions and electric field in the base region of a *pnp* transistor under low-level injection conditions ($n_b' \ll N_{bo}$).

Approximate space-charge neutrality is maintained in the base in spite of injection. The majority-carrier concentration increases in such a way that the excess hole and electron concentrations remain approximately equal. Thus, for low injection levels, the majority-carrier distribution has the form shown in Fig. 1.3b. It is important to note that the vertical scale is broken on this sketch because the equilibrium majority-carrier concentration n_{bo} is, typically, many orders of magnitude greater than p_{bo}.

Minority carriers diffuse across the base in response to the concentration gradient shown in Fig. 1.3a. This diffusion current, which accounts for transistor action, is the principal component of the emitter and collector currents. In comparison, there must be very little *net longitudinal* flow of *majority* carriers across the base *because neither junction permits any substantial flow of electrons.* Across the emitter junction the electron flow is negligible compared with the hole flow because the emitter body is doped much more heavily than the base. This is done, of course, precisely to keep the emitter injection efficiency high. At the collector junction, only those electrons which are thermally generated in the collector body can be extracted into the base.

Nonetheless, there is obviously a significant diffusion component of majority-carrier current across the base, because the majority and minority carrier concentration gradients are essentially equal. Therefore, there must be in the base a longitudinal electric field, directed *from* the emitter *to* the collector, which opposes the diffusive flow of the majority-carrier electrons. As we shall see below, this field is larger at the collector than at the emitter, as indicated in Fig. 1.3c, because the majority-carrier concentration is lower at the collector.

The longitudinal electric field in the base aids the transport of the minority carriers. In the following section we shall study this drift-aided transport in more detail. The analysis will show that the electric field has a significant influence on minority-carrier flow when the injected minority-carrier concentration $p_b(0)$ becomes comparable to the equilibrium majority-carrier concentration n_{bo}; i.e., when low-level injection no longer obtains. At this same level of collector current we should re-examine our first-order calculation of the current injected into the emitter. Also, our assumption that all of the applied emitter-base voltage appears across the space-charge layer as a change in the height of the potential barrier should be reconsidered. It will be recalled that this assumption and our calculation of current injected into the emitter were based on low-injection conditions.

1.2.1 Minority-Carrier Transport in the Base

The net longitudinal majority-carrier electron current in the base, J_{ex}, can be written in terms of its drift and diffusion components as:*

$$J_{ex} = q \left(\mu_{be} n_b \mathcal{E}_x + D_{be} \frac{dn_b}{dx} \right) \tag{1.2}$$

We assume that J_{ex} is approximately zero because the majority carrier current crossing either junction is negligible. In addition, we focus attention on a *homogeneous-base transistor*, in which $dn_b/dx \cong dp_b/dx$ as a consequence of quasi-neutrality. Therefore, the longitudinal electric field $\mathcal{E}_x$ must be given by

$$\mathcal{E}_x \cong - \left(\frac{kT}{q} \right) \frac{1}{n_b} \frac{dp_b}{dx} \tag{1.3}$$

where we have used the Einstein relation

$$\frac{D_{be}}{\mu_{be}} = \frac{D_{bh}}{\mu_{bh}} = \frac{kT}{q} \tag{1.4}$$

The net longitudinal *minority*-carrier hole current J_{hx} is

$$J_{hx} = q \left(\mu_{bh} p_b \mathcal{E}_x - D_{bh} \frac{dp_b}{dx} \right) \tag{1.5}$$

Using Eq. 1.3 to substitute for $\mathcal{E}_x$ yields

$$J_{hx} = -q D_{bh} \left(1 + \frac{p_b}{n_b} \right) \frac{dp_b}{dx} \tag{1.6}$$

which differs from the usual result obtained for the idealized first-order analysis because of the factor $(1 + p_b/n_b)$. This nonlinear factor differs negligibly from unity as long as $p_b \ll n_b$; i.e., as long as the injection level is low. However, low-level injection is exceeded in most low-power transistors for a collector current in the range from 1 to 10 ma. At larger currents the longitudinal

* ISP, Sec. 3.6.2.

electric field has the effect of increasing the minority-carrier current by the factor $(1 + p_b/n_b)$. This effect can be interpreted in terms of an "effective" diffusion constant having the value $D_{bh}(1 + p_b/n_b)$. If the current is large enough so that over most of the base region $p_b \gg n_{bo}$ or $p_b \cong n_b$, the effective diffusion constant is *doubled* by the action of the electric field.

The approximate distributions of carriers and electric field under high-level injection conditions are shown in Fig. 1.4. The carrier concentration distributions differ significantly from the triangular distributions which obtain under low-level injection conditions. Near the emitter edge of the base the drift and diffusion components of the minority-carrier current are nearly equal. Near the collector edge the same total minority-carrier current must be supported solely by diffusion (because the minority-carrier con-

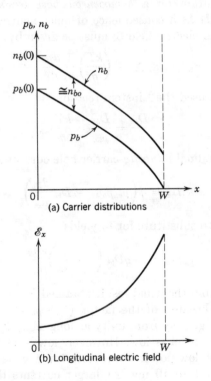

(a) Carrier distributions

(b) Longitudinal electric field

Fig. 1.4. Illustrating the consequences of high-level injection in the base.

centration becomes very small), so that the slope at the collector edge is approximately twice that at the emitter edge. Even though the electric field *increases* toward the collector, its influence on the minority-carrier current is less near the collector because of the reduced concentration of minority carriers.

As a consequence of the electric field which aids the flow of minority carriers at high injection levels, the amount of excess charge which is stored in the base for a given collector current is *reduced*. The slope of the minority-carrier distribution at $x = W$, where all the minority-carrier current results from diffusion, is proportional to the collector current. The area under the same distribution is proportional to the excess charge stored in the base. Figure 1.4a shows that the excess charge is somewhat more than one half as great as it would be if the aiding electric field were not present.

This high-level effect can be demonstrated experimentally by measuring the total excess charge stored in the base as a function of the collector current. Such data are shown in Fig. 1.5, which applies to a *pnp* germanium alloy transistor. This curve shows a drop in slope in the current range where high-level injection should start; the slope decreases by somewhat less than a factor of two, which is in general agreement with the predictions of our high-level model.

Our analysis is based on the assumption that the base region is approximately neutral. Analysis of the space-charge distribution shows that the assumption of quasi-neutrality is valid up to moderately high collector currents (see Problem P1.2).

The conclusion that high-level injection in the base causes a longitudinal electric field which *aids* the transport of minority carriers is valid only for a homogeneous-base transistor. Some diffused-base transistors have a significant gradient of the impurity concentration in the base which gives rise to a longitudinal electric field *in equilibrium*.* This electric field, which causes drift-aided transport of the minority carriers under low-level injection conditions, is reduced in magnitude and has proportionately less effect on the flow of minority carriers as the injection level increases. This occurs because the impurity charge distribution, which

* See, for example, PEM, Sec. 9.4.

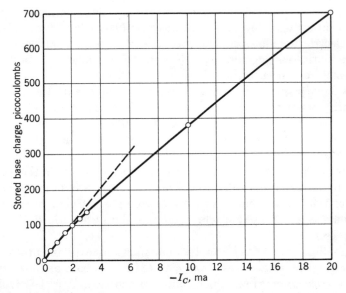

Fig. 1.5. Dependence of stored base charge on collector current for a *pnp* alloy transistor.

determines the low-injection-level field, is dominated at high injection levels by the charge distribution which results from the small deviations between the excess hole and electron concentrations. Consequently, the flow of minority carriers across the base of a transistor having an appreciable built-in field is aided *less* at high injection levels.*

1.2.2 *Carrier Injection into the Emitter at High Currents*

For good transistor performance it is desirable for the emitter current to consist primarily of base minority carriers, e.g., holes in a *pnp* transistor. This desirable condition is obtained by doping the emitter much more heavily than the base. Clearly high-level injection conditions augment the majority-carrier concentration in the base, thereby increasing the component of emitter current resulting from the injection of base majority carriers into the emitter. Our study of this effect focuses on the *emitter defect*, which

* See also ECP, Sec. 4.1.3.

is defined as the ratio of current injected into the emitter, to the collector current.* We consider a *pnp* transistor.

Both the current injected into the emitter, which must be supplied at the base terminal, and the collector current are governed by the Boltzmann relations which express the carrier concentration ratios at the emitter junction in terms of the height of the potential barrier. These ratios are

$$\frac{p_b(0)}{p_e(0)} = \frac{n_e(0)}{n_b(0)} = e^{-q\Delta\psi/kT} \tag{1.7}$$

where $\Delta\psi$ is the height of the potential barrier, $p_e(0)$ and $n_e(0)$ denote the hole and electron concentrations in the emitter at the edge of the space-charge layer, and $p_b(0)$ and $n_b(0)$ have similar meanings in terms of the hole and electron concentrations in the base.†

Inasmuch as the emitter is doped much more heavily than the base, there exists a range of collector currents within which $p_e(0)$ remains essentially equal to the corresponding equilibrium value p_{eo} while, at the same time, $n_b(0)$ may be increased significantly above n_{bo} by high-level injection in the base. In this range of collector currents the emitter defect is

$$\delta_e = \frac{(qD_e/L_e)An_e(0)}{(qD_b'/W)Ap_b(0)} = \frac{D_eWn_e(0)}{D_b'L_ep_b(0)}$$

where we have assumed that the electron current injected into the emitter is given by the usual low-injection-level expression for a *pn* junction and where D_b' denotes an *effective* diffusion constant for holes in the base. D_b' varies from D_b at low injection levels to $2D_b$ at high levels, as shown in the previous section. When Eq. 1.7 is used to express the ratio $n_e(0)/p_b(0)$ in terms of the ratio $n_b(0)/p_e(0)$, we obtain

$$\delta_e = \frac{D_eWn_b(0)}{D_b'L_ep_e(0)} \cong \frac{D_eWn_b(0)}{D_b'L_ep_{eo}} \tag{1.8}$$

At low currents, $n_b(0) \cong n_{bo}$ and the emitter defect is a constant, independent of collector current. However, as the base goes into high-level injection, $n_b(0)$ increases above n_{bo} and the defect in-

* PEM, Sec. 7.2.
† PEM, Sec. 2.3.3.

creases, which implies a greater-than-proportional increase in base current.

The increase in the current injected into the emitter, which occurs at high injection levels in the base is, of course, in conflict with the assumption made in Sec. 1.2.1 that the longitudinal majority-carrier current in the base is negligible. Certainly our analysis of the longitudinal electric field in the base will become inapplicable at collector currents and injection levels so large that the current gain from base to collector has decreased to near unity.

1.2.3 *Electrostatic Potential Drops in the Base at High Currents*

In Sec. 1.2.1 we found that there is a longitudinal electric field in the base which aids the flow of minority carriers as the injection level rises. This electric field is accompanied by longitudinal variations of the electrostatic potential in the base. There are, of course, also transverse electric fields and transverse variations of potential arising from transverse majority-carrier base currents. If there is a potential difference between the ohmic contact applied to the base region and the base material at the edge of the emitter space-charge layer, the assumption that all of the applied voltage appears as a change in the height of the potential barrier must be revised. Therefore, we now examine the distribution of electrostatic potential in the base region.

Our analysis is based on a *pnp* diffused-junction structure, shown in cross section in Fig. 1.6. The analysis is not limited to this structure and, of course, exactly analogous considerations apply in *npn* transistors.

The hole and electron currents in the base can be written in terms of their drift and diffusion components as follows:

$$\mathbf{J}_h = q(\mu_{bh} p_b \mathcal{E} - D_{bh}\nabla p_b)$$
$$\mathbf{J}_e = q(\mu_{be} n_b \mathcal{E} + D_{be}\nabla n_b) \tag{1.9a,b}$$

If we express the electric field in terms of the electrostatic potential ϕ in the base, and employ the Einstein relation (Eq. 1.4) to express D_{be} and D_{bh} in terms of μ_{be} and μ_{bh}, respectively, the *total* current, $\mathbf{J}_e + \mathbf{J}_h$, becomes:

$$\mathbf{J}_T = \mathbf{J}_e + \mathbf{J}_h$$
$$= q(\mu_{be} n_b + \mu_{bh} p_b)(-\nabla\phi) + q\frac{kT}{q}(\mu_{be}\nabla n_b - \mu_{bh}\nabla p_b) \tag{1.10}$$

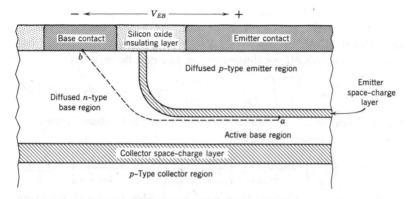

Fig. 1.6. Cross section of a planar diffused *pnp* transistor.

The factor $q(\mu_{be}n_b + \mu_{bh}p_b)$ is the conductivity of the base material σ_b. Consequently the gradient of the electrostatic potential can be written:

$$\nabla\phi = -\frac{\mathbf{J}_T}{\sigma_b} + \frac{kT}{q}\left(\frac{\mu_{be}\nabla n_b - \mu_{bh}\nabla p_b}{\mu_{be}n_b + \mu_{bh}p_b}\right)$$

The potential drop ϕ_{ab} from any point a in the base to any other point b is, therefore,

$$\phi_{ab} = \int_b^a \nabla\phi \cdot d\mathbf{s} = \frac{kT}{q}\int_b^a \left(\frac{\mu_{be}\nabla n_b - \mu_{bh}\nabla p_b}{\mu_{be}n_b + \mu_{bh}p_b}\right) \cdot d\mathbf{s} - \int_b^a \frac{\mathbf{J}_T}{\sigma_b} \cdot d\mathbf{s}$$

$$(1.11)$$

This result shows that electrostatic potential differences in the base region have two sources:

(1) The first term of Eq. 1.11 shows that a potential difference which is *not* a function of current can exist between any two points at which the carrier concentrations are different. Such distributed emfs, which, as we shall see below, are important only under high-level injection conditions, result from the small deviations from neutrality which accompany injection.

(2) The second term of Eq. 1.11 shows that a potential difference can result from "ohmic drops" associated directly with the flow of current.

We postpone discussion of the "ohmic" contributions to ϕ_{ab} until Sec. 1.3. We now evaluate the distributed emf, described by the first term of Eq. 1.11, and determine its effect on the relationship between the applied voltage and the carrier concentrations. Quasi-neutrality requires $n_b \cong N_D + p_b$. Consequently, the distributed emf, which we designate as ϕ'_{ab}, can be written:

$$\phi'_{ab} = \frac{kT}{q} \int_b^a \frac{(\mu_{be} - \mu_{bh})}{(\mu_{be} + \mu_{bh})n_b - \mu_{bh}N_D} \nabla n_b \cdot d\mathbf{s} \qquad (1.12a)$$

which, because N_D is constant for a homogeneous-base transistor, can be integrated to yield

$$\phi'_{ab} = \left(\frac{kT}{q}\right) \frac{\mu_{be} - \mu_{bh}}{\mu_{be} + \mu_{bh}} \ln \left[\frac{(\mu_{be} + \mu_{bh})n_b(a) - \mu_{bh}N_D}{(\mu_{be} + \mu_{bh})n_b(b) - \mu_{bh}N_D}\right] \qquad (1.12b)$$

Clearly this potential drop vanishes under low-level injection conditions for which $n_b(a) \cong n_b(b) \cong n_{bo}$. However, when the injection level is high, ϕ'_b contributes significantly to ϕ_{ab}. If we consider the potential drop along any path connecting a point a at the edge of the emitter space-charge layer with a point b at the base contact (such a path is shown in Fig. 1.6), it is apparent that there is a nonohmic potential drop whenever low-level injection conditions are exceeded. In our previous notation:

$$n_b(a) = n_b(0)$$

and if the base contact is "ohmic"

$$n_b(b) = n_{bo}$$

The corresponding approximate drop, assuming $n_b(0) \gg n_{bo} \gg p_{bo}$, is, from Eq. 1.12b,

$$\phi'_{ab} \cong \left(\frac{kT}{q}\right)\left(\frac{\mu_{be} - \mu_{bh}}{\mu_{be} + \mu_{bh}}\right) \ln \left[\left(1 + \frac{\mu_{bh}}{\mu_{be}}\right) \frac{n_b(0)}{n_{bo}}\right] \qquad (1.13)$$

Inasmuch as $\mu_{be} > \mu_{bh}$ for both silicon and germanium, ϕ'_{ab} is positive. That is, the potential at the edge of the emitter space-charge layer is higher than the potential at the base contact.

The physical origin of this potential drop is easily understood in terms of the *transverse* distributions of the excess carriers. The hole and electron concentrations fall from large values near the space-charge layer to equilibrium values at the base contact. Therefore, both holes and electrons tend to diffuse from the active base region toward the base contact. The transverse electric field associated with ϕ'_{ab}, i.e., $-\nabla\phi'_{ab}$, is likewise directed from the active base region toward the base contact so that it aids the flow of the holes, which have the smaller mobility, and reduces the flow of the electrons, which have the larger mobility. The distribution and magnitude of ϕ'_{ab} are such that the total current vanishes when $\phi_{ab} = \phi'_{ab}$. Note, however, that the total current vanishes not because the hole and electron fluxes or particle currents are separately zero, but because ϕ'_{ab} *forces* the hole and electron fluxes to be exactly equal.*

Although Eq. 1.13 was derived for a *pnp* transistor, the corresponding result for an *npn* transistor differs only in that the term in brackets is

$$\left[\left(1 + \frac{\mu_{be}}{\mu_{bh}} \right) \frac{p_b(0)}{p_{bo}} \right]$$

The *polarity* of ϕ'_{ab} is unchanged, in accordance with the physical mechanism described in the preceding paragraph.

Now that we have evaluated the nonohmic distributed emf, ϕ'_{ab}, and have found that it corresponds to a potential *drop* between the base region and the base contact for both *pnp* and *npn* transistors, we determine its effect on the emitter-base voltage. In general, the applied emitter-base voltage V_{EB} divides between the space-charge layer and the base-region potential drop ϕ_{ab}. Specifically:

$$V_{EB} = V_{EB}^{(J)} + \phi_{ab}$$

where $V_{EB}^{(J)}$ denotes the change in the height of the potential barrier at the emitter space-charge layer. If ϕ_{ab} is expressed in terms of the nonohmic term, ϕ'_{ab}, and the transverse ohmic drop, which is given by the second term of Eq. 1.11, the applied voltage may be written as

$$V_{EB} = V_{EB}^{(J)} + \phi'_{ab} + \text{(ohmic drop)}$$

We consider the nature and consequences of the ohmic drop in Sec. 1.3. Therefore, we now focus attention on the applied emitter base voltage reduced by the ohmic drop, and denote this fictitious "emitter-base" voltage by $V_{EB'}$. That is

$$V_{EB'} = V_{EB} - \text{(ohmic drop)}$$
$$= V_{EB}^{(J)} + \phi'_{ab}$$

* Such a potential drop is encountered in certain photovoltaic devices, where it is known as the *Dember potential*.

Introduction of the variable $V_{EB'}$ emphasizes the fact that $V_{EB}^{(J)}$, the change in the height of the potential barrier at the emitter junction, differs from the applied voltage, *even if there are no ohmic drops*, if the injection level in the base is high. The amount of this difference is just ϕ'_{ab}, the nonohmic distributed emf given by Eq. 1.13. For *pnp* transistors in the normal region of operation (forward-biased emitter, reverse-biased collector) V_{EB} and $V_{EB}^{(J)}$ are, of course, positive; ϕ'_{ab} is, as discussed above, positive. Consequently, *in pnp transistors*, the nonohmic distributed emf which appears at high injection levels causes the change in height of the potential barrier to be *less than* the fictitious applied voltage $V_{EB'}$. For *npn* transistors, V_{EB} and $V_{EB}^{(J)}$, are *negative* in the normal region of operation but ϕ'_{ab} is still positive. Thus, the nonohmic distributed emf causes $V_{EB}^{(J)}$ to be *greater than* the fictitious applied voltage $V_{EB'}$ in *npn* transistors.

We now explore the consequences of the nonohmic distributed emf in terms of the relationship between the injected excess-carrier concentration and the junction voltage. Our analysis is for a *pnp* transistor. The Boltzmann factor at the emitter junction requires:

$$V_{EB}^{(J)} = \frac{kT}{q} \ln \frac{p_b(0)}{p_{bo}}$$

Therefore

$$V_{EB'} = \frac{kT}{q} \ln \left[\frac{p_b(0) n_b(0)^m (1 + \mu_{bh}/\mu_{be})^m}{p_{bo} n_{bo}{}^m} \right] \quad (1.14a)$$

where

$$m = \frac{\mu_{be} - \mu_{bh}}{\mu_{be} + \mu_{bh}} \quad (1.14b)$$

However, under high-level injection conditions $n_b(0) \cong p_b(0)$, and Eq. 1.14a yields:

$$p_b(0) \cong \sqrt[1+m]{\frac{p_{bo} n_{bo}{}^m}{(1 + \mu_{bh}/\mu_{be})^m}} \, e^{q V_{EB'}/(1+m)kT} \quad (1.15)$$

The parameter m decreases with decreasing resistivity from a maximum of about 0.35 in germanium and about 0.45 in silicon. Equation 1.15 shows that in *pnp* transistors operating at high-injection levels (high collector currents) the dependence of the injected carrier concentration on $V_{EB'}$ is not as strong as it is for low-injection levels. The corresponding result for npn units differs only in that $(1 + m)$ is replaced by $(1 - m)$. Consequently, in npn transistors at high-injection levels the dependence of injected carrier concentration of $V_{EB'}$ is stronger than it is for low-injection levels.

It is possible to demonstrate one effect of this potential drop in the base region by observing the dependence of the collector current, which in a pnp transistor is approximately proportional to $p_b(0)/W$, on the emitter-base voltage V_{EB}. We must do so under experimental conditions which guarantee that the *transverse components* of the total base current $\mathbf{J}_T$ are negligible, to avoid the ohmic term in Eq.1.11. That is, we seek conditions such that $\mathbf{J}_T \cdot d\mathbf{s} \cong 0$ for some path S from the base contact to the edge of the space-charge layer in the active base region. Under ordinary circumstances this ohmic term dominates V_{EB} at high current levels. We shall see in Sec. 1.6 that the transistor can be operated with negligible transverse base current in the avalanche mode. Consequently, measurements made under avalanche conditions should demonstrate the effect of ϕ'_{ab}. Such data are shown in Fig. 1.7. The reduction in slope at high current levels is apparent. For comparison we also show the dependence of collector current on emitter-base voltage under normal operating conditions for which $\mathbf{J}_T \cdot d\mathbf{s}$ is *not* zero. The ohmic contributions to V_{EB} are apparent in the deviation in the high-current region of this curve from that obtained under avalanche mode conditions.

1.2.4 *Summary of Effects Associated with High-Level Injection in the Base*

At a level of collector current which lies in the range from 1 to 10 ma for most low-power transistors, the minority-carrier concentration in the active base region becomes comparable to the equilibrium majority-carrier concentration and the majority-carrier concentration increases significantly above its equilibrium value. This increase in majority-carrier concentration has three consequences:

(1) A longitudinal electric field in the base influences the flow of both types of excess carriers. This field opposes the diffusion of

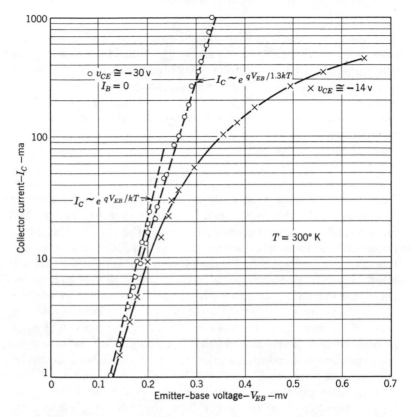

Fig. 1.7. Collector current versus emitter-base voltage for a *pnp* germanium alloy transistor (from G. L. Parker "High-Current Transverse Base Voltage Measurements in Transistors", unpublished E.E. M.S. thesis, M.I.T., June, 1964). These data are corrected for voltage drops in the internal emitter lead, and for the dependence of base width on collector current and voltage. Note that the dashed lines signify theoretical asymptotes while the solid curve links experimental points taken with $I_b \neq 0$.

majority carriers and aids the diffusion of minority carriers. At high levels of collector current this field has an effect equivalent to doubling the minority-carrier diffusion constant in the base.

(2) The injection of base majority carriers into the emitter is enhanced. At high collector currents this effect, which can be interpreted as an increase in the emitter defect, causes the base current to increase at a greater rate than the collector current.

(3) In addition to the ohmic drop, a concentration-dependent electrostatic potential drop appears between the base material at the edge of the emitter space-charge layer and the base contact. At high collector currents this drop becomes comparable to the change in the height of the potential barrier, so that the injected minority-carrier concentration varies as $e^{qV_{EB'}/(1\pm m)kT}$ rather than as $e^{qV_{EB'}/kT}$. The plus sign applies to a *pnp* transistor, the minus sign to an *npn* transistor, and m is of the order of 0.4.

1.3 TRANSVERSE OHMIC VOLTAGE DROPS IN THE BASE REGION

The flow of majority carriers in the base region of a transistor is associated with ohmic voltage drops which significantly influence the performance of the transistor at high current levels. Majority carriers flow in the base in a direction parallel to the junctions and normal to the longitudinal diffusive flow of the minority carriers which account for transistor action. The sources of this majority-carrier flow are, under static conditions, as follows.

(1) Recombination of majority carriers with injected minority carriers on the surfaces and in the emitter space-charge layer, as well as in the neutral base region.

(2) Injection of base-region majority carriers into the emitter.

(3) Extraction of base-region majority carriers from the collector (where they are, of course, minority carriers).

(4) When the collector-base voltage is high, avalanche multiplication of carriers in the collector space-charge layer produces an additional flow of base-region majority carriers from the collector junction to the base.

Under dynamic conditions, additional components of base current are required:

(5) Base-region majority carriers are required to change the charge stored in the junction space-charge layers whenever the junction voltages change with time.

(6) Similarly, carriers are required to change the excess charge stored in the quasi-neutral base region (and possibly even in the quasi-neutral emitter region) whenever the collector current changes with time.

For fast changes in the terminal voltages or currents, these dynamic components of the transverse base current can be much larger than the static components.

The transverse majority-carrier currents in the base flow principally by drift and therefore are associated with transverse electrostatic potential drops in the base region. These potential drops cause the voltages which appear across the emitter and collector space-charge layers to differ from the voltages which are applied at the terminals of the transistor. In addition, they cause *transverse* variations in both the injected carrier concentrations and in the longitudinal minority-carrier flow, and these variations are of major importance in transistor operation at high levels of collector current. We now explore the nature and consequences of these transverse ohmic voltage drops.

1.3.1 *Components of the Transverse Ohmic Voltage Drops*

As a vehicle for our discussion we consider a *pnp* alloy-junction transistor having the cross section shown in Fig. 1.8. It is convenient to think of the neutral base as divided into two regions. The region contained between the emitter and collector junctions having width W is called the *active base region*. This active region is characterized by high concentrations of injected minority carriers, and transistor action takes place in this region. The remainder of

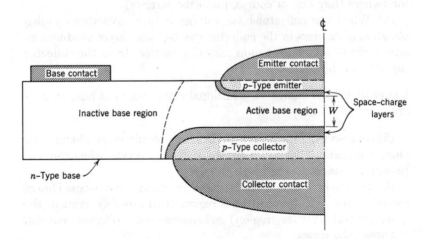

Fig. 1.8. Cross section of an alloy junction *pnp* transistor.

the base material is called the *inactive base region*. It is useful to think in terms of these two regions, even though the boundary between them is defined somewhat arbitrarily.

Clearly all of the base current must pass through the inactive base region to reach the active portion of the base. Although the carrier concentrations in the inactive region may be disturbed from their thermal equilibrium values by minority-carrier injection, transistor action does not occur here, and the voltage drops produced in this region by base current can be modeled quite accurately by a lumped resistance in series with the base terminal. This resistance, which is sometimes called the *extrinsic* base resistance, usually lies in the range from 10 to 100 ohms for most low-power transistors. If, as is often the case, most of the inactive base region is subject to minority-carrier injection, this lumped resistance must decrease with increasing collector current to reflect the "conductivity modulation" which occurs there.

The phenomena which occur in the active base region are more complicated because the majority carrier base current decreases to zero toward the geometrical center of the transistor and because transverse ohmic drops in the active region cause nonuniform minority-carrier injection. That is, the forward bias voltage which appears across the emitter space-charge layer is less near the center of the active region than near the periphery, because the transverse ohmic drop in the active base region subtracts from the applied emitter-base voltage. Notice that negligible transverse voltage drops occur in the emitter body because it has such a high conductivity. Consequently, portions of the active region near the center of the transistor operate at lower concentrations of injected minority carriers, and thus at lower longitudinal minority-carrier current density, than do portions near the inactive base region. Because of the exponential dependence of the injected carrier concentration on voltage, the nonuniform distribution of minority carriers can be quite pronounced. It takes a transverse ohmic drop of only about 25 mv to reduce the longitudinal minority-carrier current density by a factor of e^{-1}. Because transverse ohmic drops cause minority-carrier injection to be concentrated near the edges of the emitter region, this phenomenon is often called *emitter crowding* or *pinch-out*. The important features of the transverse potential distribution in the base, and of the associated nonuniform minority-carrier distributions, are shown in Fig. 1.9.

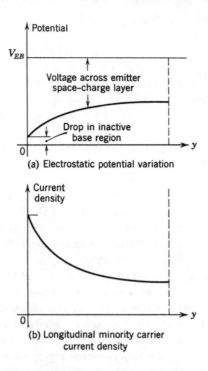

(a) Electrostatic potential variation

(b) Longitudinal minority carrier current density

Fig. 1.9. Illustrating pinch-out in a *pnp* transistor. The transverse coordinate in the base region is designated as y, and $y = 0$ corresponds to the edge of the active base legion.

The pinch-out mechanism illustrated in Fig. 1.9 restricts transistor action to the periphery of the emitter region at high collector currents. For this reason, modern transistor designs arrange the emitter and base contacts to provide the greatest possible effective periphery. Two techniques which are intended to minimize pinchout are shown in Fig. 1.10. The scheme of Fig. 1.10a has been extended to an arrangement with many alternating thin emitter and base contacts or "fingers." Such an arrangement is referred to as an *interdigital* configuration. For the same reason, the ring base contact scheme of Fig. 1.10b is sometimes modified to make the emitter a ring with additional base contact in the form of a disc inside the emitter ring. Another useful configuration distorts the rings into star-shaped plates, resulting in a greater effective periph-

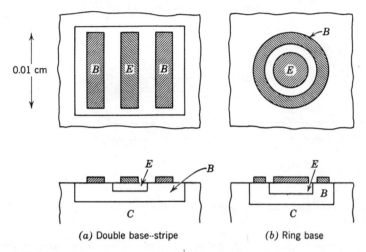

(*a*) Double base–stripe   (*b*) Ring base

Fig. 1.10. Transistor structures which minimize the resistance of the inactive base region and pinch-out effects.

ery. All of these structural arrangements tend to reduce the resistance of the inactive region in addition to minimizing pinch-out.

1.3.2 *Analysis of the Active Base Region for Low-Level Injection*

To investigate some of the quantitative features of transverse ohmic voltage drops in the active base region we consider the physical model shown in Fig. 1.11. This model applies to a structure having rectangular geometry, such as that shown in Fig. 1.10*a*, where $y = h$ denotes the midplane of the emitter. Analogous calculations can be made for structures having cylindrical symmetry. We assume that the base region has a uniform resistivity ρ. Consequently our analysis is valid only for low-level injection situations in which the majority-carrier concentration is essentially undisturbed by injection.

We consider a *pnp* transistor and designate as $V(y)$ the portion of the applied emitter-base voltage which appears across the emitter-base barrier, i.e., $V(y)$ is the reduction with bias of the emitter-junction potential barrier at the plane which cuts the junctions at a distance y from the edge of the emitter. The corresponding reduction in barrier height at the edge of the emitter, where $y = 0$, is denoted by V_0. Of course, $V_0 > V(y)$ because of

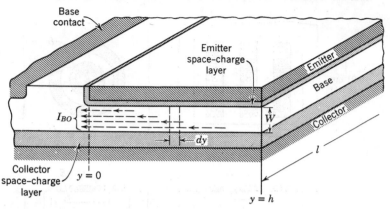

Fig. 1.11. Model used in analysis of transverse ohmic voltage drops in the base.

the transverse ohmic drops in the base. The total base current which *leaves* the active region at $y = 0$ is I_{B0}, while the base current which remains at y is $I_B(y)$. Both $I_B(y)$ and I_{B0} are positive quantities in the directions illustrated, and the physical effect in a *pnp* transistor is the flow of *electrons* from the base contact *into* the active base region.*

Consider a differential element of thickness dy. This element makes a contribution to the total collector current (neglecting the extraction of electrons from the collector) of

$$d(-I_C) = qD_b l dy \left. \frac{p_b(y)}{W} \right|_{\text{emitter edge}}$$

$$= \frac{qD_b l p_{bo}}{W} e^{qV(y)/kT} dy$$

(1.16a)

If we designate the total (emitter plus base) defect† of the transistor as δ, the base current crossing the differential element must *decrease* in distance dy by an amount $\delta d(-I_C)$. That is,

$$dI_B = - \frac{\delta q D_b l p_{bo}}{W} e^{qV(y)/kT} dy$$

(1.16b)

---

* If the collector-base voltage exceeds the sustaining voltage (see Sec. 1.6), the direction of flow of base current is reversed. We exclude this possibility as well as the normal collector saturation current in our analysis. Note that the sign definition for I_B is valid for this section *only*.

† PEM, Sec. 7.2.

The ohmic voltage drop across the differential element of resistance $\rho dy/Wl$ is

$$dV = -\frac{\rho}{Wl} I_B \, dy \tag{1.16c}$$

If $V(y)$ is eliminated between Eqs. 1.16b and 1.16c, we obtain the following nonlinear differential equation for I_B:

$$\frac{d^2 I_B}{dy^2} = -\frac{q}{kT}\frac{\rho}{Wl} I_B \frac{dI_B}{dy} \tag{1.17}$$

The boundary conditions which apply to solutions of this differential equation are

$$I_B = I_{B0} \quad \text{for} \quad y = 0$$
$$I_B = 0 \quad \text{for} \quad y = h$$

The solution of Eq. 1.17 which satisfies these boundary conditions is

$$I_B = I_{B0} \frac{\tan \gamma(h - y)}{\tan \gamma h} \tag{1.18}$$

where the constant γ satisfies the relation:

$$2\gamma h \tan \gamma h = \frac{q}{kT} I_{B0} r_B \tag{1.19a}$$

in which r_B is the *transverse resistance* of the base region

$$r_B = \frac{\rho h}{Wl} \tag{1.19b}$$

The corresponding distribution of the emitter junction voltage is, from integration of Eq. 1.16c,

$$V(y) = V_0 - \frac{2kT}{q} \ln \left(\frac{\cos \gamma(h - y)}{\cos \gamma h} \right) \tag{1.20}$$

Finally the collector current density $d(-I_C)/l dy$ is, from Eqs. 1.16a and 1.20:

$$J(y) = \frac{1}{l}\frac{d(-I_C)}{dy} = J_0 \left[\frac{\cos \gamma h}{\cos \gamma(h - y)} \right]^2 \tag{1.21}$$

where J_0 is the collector current density at $x = 0$

$$J_0 = \frac{qD_b p_{bo}}{W} e^{qV_0/kT}$$

The consequences of transverse ohmic drops in the base region are illustrated in Fig. 1.12 where Eqs. 1.18, 1.20, and 1.21 are plotted for several values of the parameter $(q/kT)I_{B0}r_B$. These curves show the phenomenon of pinch-out, which appears as I_{B0} and thus I_C increases.

It is *not* possible to model the effects shown in Fig. 1.12 by adding a constant lumped resistance in the base lead, except at low levels of collector current where pinch-out is not present and where low-level injection conditions hold in the base. For small enough values of base current the effects of transverse voltage drops on the collector current *can* be represented by adding in the external base lead a base resistance of $r_x = r_B/3$, where r_B is the resistance defined by Eq. 1.19b (see Problem P1.6). Whereas the modeling of transverse voltage drops is quite simple for this limiting situation, it turns out that the voltage drop across the base resistance is seldom of consequence in the current range for which the model is valid. Unfortunately, in those high-current situations where transverse voltage drops in the base really matter, it is not possible to represent their effects by means of a *constant* lumped base resistance.

Of course, it is possible to define a variable resistance, which is a function of collector current, and to choose it to account correctly for the effects of transverse voltage drops on the dc collector current.* This representation in terms of a dc base resistance is of limited usefulness in modeling the dc behavior of the transistor, however, just because the required resistance *is* current-dependent.

It is necessary to use caution in applying the analysis of this section to real transistors. In most practical situations the low-level injection condition is exceeded at about the same time that pinch-out develops, and the two effects interact. Consequently, the preceding analysis must be modified to account for modulation of the base resistivity.

---

* See, for example, PEM, Sec. 8.2.

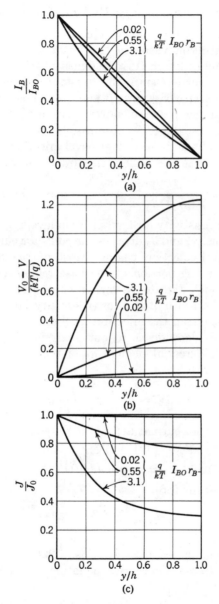

Fig. 1.12. Calculated distribution of transverse base current, transverse ohmic voltage drop, and longitudinal minority-carrier current density, for several values of base current. Low-level injection is assumed.

1.3.3 *Modifications Required for High-Level Injection*

When the base is in high-level injection ($n_b \cong p_b$), the majority-carrier concentration varies in the *longitudinal* direction and is proportional to collector current density. It follows that these excess majority carriers lower the resistance of the base region to the flow of transverse base current and cause most of the transverse base current to flow near the emitter edge of the base because the resistivity is lowest there. To obtain some estimates of the effects of transverse voltage drops in high-level injection, we *assume* that the resistivity of the base region has a *transverse* variation given by

$$\rho = \rho_o \frac{J_1}{J(y) + J_1} \cong \rho_o \frac{J_1}{J(y)} \qquad \text{for} \quad J(y) \gg J_1 \quad (1.22a)$$

where ρ_o is the resistivity for low injection levels, $J(y)$ is the collector current density, and J_1 denotes the collector current density at which high-level injection begins. Most of the transverse base current flows in the portion of the base region near the emitter junction in which the excess-carrier concentration is high. We denote by w the width of this low-resistivity portion of the base. Clearly w depends on the injection level and thus varies with I_C. We neglect this dependence in our analysis. The ohmic voltage drop across a differential element dy of the low-resistivity region is, by analogy with Eq. 1.16c,

$$dV = -\frac{\rho_o}{wl} I_B \frac{J_1}{J(y)} dy \qquad (1.22b)$$

The change in base current across the differential element can be written, by analogy with Eq. 1.16b,

$$dI_B = -\delta l J(y) dy \qquad (1.22c)$$

where $J(y)$ is of the form

$$J(y) = \frac{2qD_b p_{bo}}{W} e^{qV(y)/kT} \qquad (1.22d)$$

If $V(y)$ is eliminated between Eqs. 1.22b to 1.22d, we obtain the following *linear* differential equation for the base current distribution:

$$\frac{d^2 I_B}{dy^2} = \left(\delta \frac{q}{kT} \frac{\rho_o J_1}{w} \right) I_B \qquad (1.23)$$

Inasmuch as this equation is linear and independent of the current level at which the transistor is operating (providing the transistor is well into high-level injection and the dependence of w and δ on I_C is neglected), we conclude that the transverse distance over which transistor action occurs is *independent* of the operating conditions and is governed solely by the parameters and structure of the device. The general solution of Eq. 1.23 is a sum of two exponentials of real argument, having a characteristic length:

$$\xi = \sqrt{\frac{kT}{q}\frac{w}{\delta \rho_o J_1}} \tag{1.24a}$$

Consequently the base current distribution must have the general form shown in Fig. 1.13. The shape of this distribution is independent of the current level, and only the current scale changes as the base and collector currents change. Pinch-out is, of course, extremely pronounced, and most of the collector current flows over a peripheral portion of the base having a transverse dimension of ξ.

We can estimate this dimension by assuming the following representative parameters:

$$\delta = 0.05$$
$$w = 1 \text{ micron}$$
$$W = 5 \text{ microns}$$

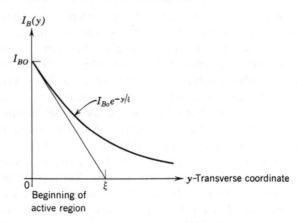

Fig. 1.13. Approximate transverse base current distribution under high-level injection conditions.

We *define* J_1 as the longitudinal current density at which $p_b(0)$ is approximately equal to the equilibrium majority carrier concentration n_{bo}. That is,

$$J_1 \cong \frac{q D_b n_{bo}}{W}$$

If this expression for J_1 is substituted into Eq. 1.24a, and if the hole and electron mobilities are assumed to be equal, the following result is obtained:

$$\xi = \sqrt{\frac{w W}{\delta}} \qquad (1.24b)$$

Use of the representative numerical values yields $\xi = 10$ microns. This result, which is based on a fairly crude approximate analysis, shows that at very high current levels, transistor action occurs only at the very edge of the emitter region. The total transverse dimension of the base region of a transistor is usually at least an order of magnitude greater than the base width. For the parameter values selected here, the penetration depth over which most of the collector current flows is only about twice the width of the neutral base region. This conclusion emphasizes the importance of using transistor structures which maximize the periphery of the emitter if operation at large values of collector current is desired.

1.3.4 *Summary of the Effects of Transverse Base Voltage Drops*

Transverse base currents cause ohmic voltage drops through the entire base region of the transistor. For purposes of analysis it is convenient to divide the base material into two regions. The *inactive* base region lies outside the emitter and collector junctions. It simply provides a conducting path from the base terminal to the *active* base region, where transistor action occurs.

Transverse voltage drops in the inactive base region can be modeled by a lumped resistance which is connected in the base lead. However, this resistance is dependent on collector current at high current levels where the conductivity of the inactive base region is increased by the excess carriers. Voltage drops in the active region cannot be modeled in terms of a lumped base resistance except under low-level conditions for which these transverse voltage drops are of little significance anyway. Active region voltage drops cause the portions of the base which are most remote from the base terminal to operate at lower longitudinal current density. This effect leads to pinch-out, which, under high-level injection conditions, causes most of the transistor action to occur only at the periphery of the emitter region.

The principal features and consequences of transverse voltage drops in the base are shown in Figs. 1.14 and 1.15, which apply to the transistor structure illustrated in Fig. 1.8. The distributions shown in Fig. 1.14 presume low-level injection in the base region in addition to negligible pinch-out. In contrast, Fig. 1.15 applies for high-level injection in most of the active base region and describes an operating condition in which there is pinch-out. The longitudinal slant of the potential distribution in Fig. 1.15a results from the longitudinal electric field considered in Sec. 1.2.1.

1.4 COLLECTOR BODY RESISTANCE

The minority carriers which are injected by the emitter into the base of a transistor under normal operating conditions are swept into the collector region by the electric field in the collector space-charge layer. These carriers are in the majority in the collector and move to the collector terminal primarily by drift. Consequently, there is an ohmic voltage drop across the collector body. This voltage drop can usually be modeled quite accurately by a constant lumped resistance in the collector lead for transistor operation in the normal mode. In the saturation region of operation with large collector currents this simple representation may become inaccurate because there may then be significant modulation of the collector conductivity by minority carriers injected into the collector from the base.

The collector resistance is usually quite negligible in alloy transistors, which have extremely thin collector regions of very low resistivity. On the other hand, collector resistance can be quite significant in diffused transistors, which have wider collector regions of higher resistivity.

Ohmic drops in the collector have an important effect on the electrical characteristics of the transistor only when the transistor is used as a switch, and then only when it is in the saturation region of operation or the ON state.* Ideally, the collector-to-emitter

---

* ECP, Sec. 2.3.1.

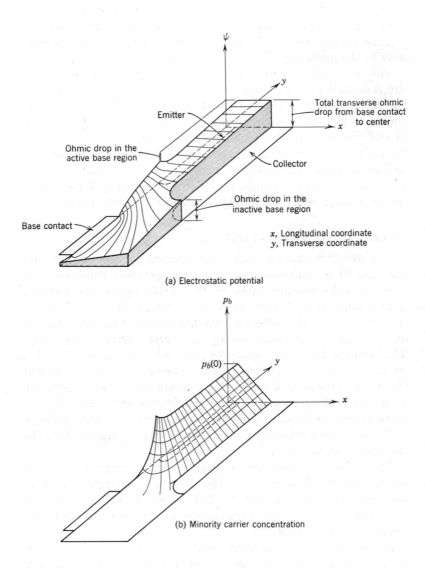

(a) Electrostatic potential

(b) Minority carrier concentration

Fig. 1.14. Potential and minority-carrier distributions in the base region of a transistor operated in low-level injection and with negligible pinch-out.

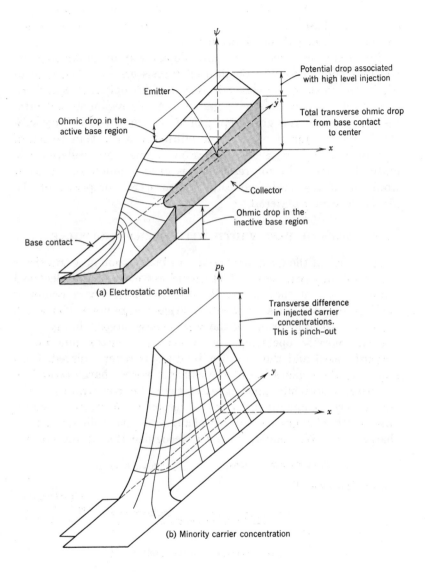

Fig. 1.15. Potential and minority-carrier distributions in the base region of a transistor operated in high-level injection and having appreciable pinch-out.

voltage of the ON transistor switch should be much smaller than the emitter-base voltage. Voltage drops in the collector region can be the principal contribution to V_{CE}.

Epitaxial growth techniques provide one way of minimizing the collector body resistance of diffused transistors. As illustrated in Fig. 1.16, most of the collector region of an epitaxial transistor consists of very-low-resistivity material. A thin region of moderate-resistivity material is grown epitaxially on the low-resistivity substrate, and the junctions are then diffused into this thin region of moderate resistivity. Since the region of moderate resistivity is quite thin, the collector resistance is clearly much less than it would be if the entire collector region were comprised of the higher-resistivity material.

1.5 CHANGES OF BASE WIDTH WITH OPERATING POINT

The width of the quasi-neutral active base region of a transistor is a significant parameter which influences most of the electrical characteristics of the device. Because the active base region is bounded on both sides by junction space-charge layers, its width changes as the dimensions of the space-charge layers change.

Under normal operating conditions the emitter junction is forward-biased and the collector junction is reverse-biased. Consequently the penetration of the collector space-charge layer into the base is normally much greater than the penetration of the emitter space-charge layer. For this reason we focus attention on base width changes caused by changes in the collector space-charge layer. We should, however, recognize that if the emitter

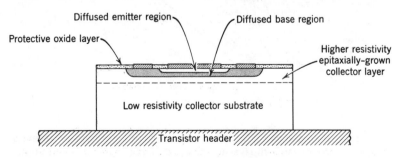

Fig. 1.16. Epitaxial planar transistor structure (not to scale).

junction becomes reverse-biased, as it may in some switching applications, considerations similar to those investigated in this section hold true at the emitter junction.

1.5.1 *Dependence of Base Width on Collector Voltage*

The general form of the distributions of space charge and electric field in the space-charge layers of a transistor is shown in Fig. 1.17. The distributions shown apply to a *pnp* alloy junction transistor

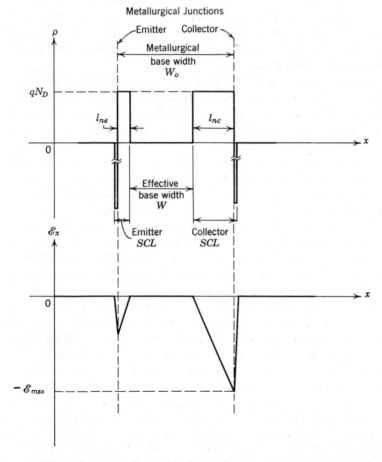

Fig. 1.17. Distributions of charge and electric field in the space-charge layers of a *pnp* alloy junction transistor under normal conditions of operation.

for which the emitter and collector are doped much more heavily than the base. The width W of the quasi-neutral base region is clearly less than the metallurgical base width W_o. As the reverse-bias voltage on the collector junction increases still further, the collector space-charge layer penetration l_{nc} increases and the effective base width is still further reduced. In some transistors it is possible for the effective base width to be reduced to zero by this mechanism, and this condition is known as *punch-through*. In a punch-through condition, the transistor behaves as though the emitter and collector were tied together by a fixed voltage source, and the base appears connected to both through a reverse-biased junction.* Normal transistor action ceases as soon as the punch-through voltage is reached.

Punch-through can be demonstrated with the circuit shown in Fig. 1.18a. For values of the collector-base voltage less than the punch-through voltage V_p, the emitter-base voltage is nearly zero. For voltages in excess of V_p, the emitter voltage rises at the same rate as the collector voltage, as shown in Fig. 1.18b. The common-emitter collector characteristics of the same transistor are shown in Fig. 1.18c, which demonstrates that the incremental resistance of the emitter-collector circuit is, indeed, very small when punch-through occurs.

It is necessary to operate transistors well below the punch-through voltage if uniform, reproducible circuit performance is required. Because the base width varies greatly in magnitude as the collector-base voltage approaches V_p, there are radical changes in those characteristics which depend on base width. In any population of a given transistor type there is a statistical distribution of punch-through voltage values. If we design to operate near the minimum value of V_p, those devices having larger values of V_p will differ widely in performance from those having smaller values. For this reason, it is seldom desirable to operate with V_{CB} greater than about one-half the punch-through voltage.

---

* It is, of course, possible to increase the collector-emitter voltage above the value at which punch-through occurs. However, the dynamic impedance presented by the transistor in punch-through is very low, and large currents are produced. In fact, the current is large enough so that the associated *mobile* carriers then constitute a significant component of the space charge in the space-charge layer that extends from emitter to collector, and the mobile space charge becomes important in limiting the current.

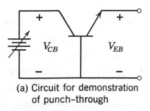

(a) Circuit for demonstration
of punch-through

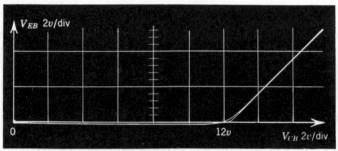

(b) Transfer characteristic

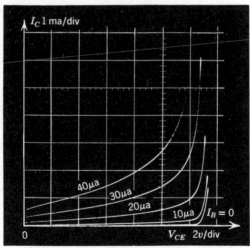

(c) Corresponding common–emitter
collector characteristics

Fig. 1.18. Punch-through in a transistor.

The punch-through condition cannot be reached at all in many transistors because, as the collector-base voltage is increased, avalanche breakdown of the collector junction occurs first. Most diffused-base transistors behave in this way. They do not show punch-through because the collector space-charge layer cannot penetrate very far into the heavily-doped portion of the base region near the emitter.

1.5.2 *Dependence of Base Width on Collector Current*

Transistor action results from base-region minority carriers which move through the junction space-charge layers by drift. At values of the electric field over about 10^3 volts per cm the carrier drift velocity is no longer proportional to the electric field.* For fields of about 2×10^4 v/cm the drift velocity approaches a saturation value of about 10^7 cm/sec (near the thermal velocity). The electric field in the collector-junction space-charge layer is usually large enough so that carriers drift at this maximum or saturation drift velocity over much of the space-charge layer.

Inasmuch as the drift velocity is limited, increases in collector current require increased numbers of minority carriers undergoing transit of the space-charge layer. Ultimately, the space charge associated with the base-region minority carriers, which drift through the space-charge layer, becomes comparable to the space charge of immobile donors and acceptors, and the total charge distribution in the space-charge layer changes accordingly.

The mobile charge carriers add to the immobile charge density in the base portion of the space-charge layer and subtract from the immobile charge density in the collector portion. If the two space-charge distributions, shown in Fig. 1.19 which is drawn for a *pnp* transistor, correspond to the *same* value of reverse voltage at the collector junction, they must have the same first moment about the metallurgical junction. Consequently the entire space-charge layer tends to shift toward the collector to accommodate the change in charge density caused by the mobile carriers. This effect is often called *base stretching*. In transistors having heavily doped collectors, this phenomenon causes the base to widen to nearly its full metallurgical length at very high collector-current densities.

* See Ref. 1.2.

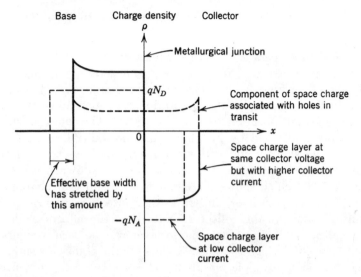

Fig. 1.19. Base stretching at high collector currents.

In transistors having a diffused collector, which is doped more heavily deeper in the collector body than near the metallurgical junction, the base region can actually be pushed back into the collector body, producing very large base width extensions at high collector current densities.

The charge contributed to the space-charge layer by the mobile carriers of course changes the relationship between the peak electric field and the voltage applied to the space-charge layer. Consequently, the apparent avalanche breakdown voltage of the junction changes. If the base is doped more heavily than the collector, the mobile carriers have the effect of reducing the magnitude of the charge density on the lightly doped side (the collector). Therefore, the reverse voltage required to attain a field large enough to produce avalanche breakdown is increased.* In other words, the apparent breakdown voltage of the junction increases. On the other hand, if the collector is doped more heavily than the base, the mobile carriers have the effect of increasing the magnitude of the charge density on the lightly-doped side, thereby reducing the apparent breakdown voltage.

* See, for example, PEM, Sec. 4.4.1.

1.6 AVALANCHE MULTIPLICATION IN THE COLLECTOR JUNCTION

Transistors operated at large values of collector-base voltage have their electrical characteristics modified by avalanche multiplication of carriers in the collector space-charge layer. For operation in the common-base configuration, the consequences of this avalanche multiplication are straightforward. The collector current is simply multiplied by M, the avalanche multiplication factor, which rises sharply and without apparent limit as the collector-base voltage approaches the avalanche breakdown voltage V_a. Figure 1.20, which shows the common-base collector characteristics of an *npn* transistor, illustrates the consequences of avalanche multiplication at the collector. Note that the effects of carrier multiplication in the space-charge layer can be seen at voltages well below V_a, which is about 98 volts for the transistor shown in Fig. 1.20. For example, at about 60 volts the collector current exceeds the emitter current in magnitude because of carrier multiplication in the collector junction.

The consequences of avalanche multiplication are more complicated and subtle when the transistor is operated in the common-emitter configuration. Holes and electrons are produced *in pairs* by the avalanche multiplication process in the collector junction. Carriers of the collector-majority type are swept into the collector by the electric field and contribute directly to the collector current.

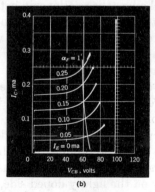

(b)

Fig. 1.20. Common-base collector characteristics, showing the effects of avalanche multiplication and breakdown at the collector junction. The locus of points at which $I_C = I_E$ ($\alpha_F = 1$) has been added.

Carriers of the opposite type are swept into the *base* region where they *reduce* the base current which must be supplied externally. If the avalanche multiplication factor becomes large enough, the polarity of the base current actually reverses, because the avalanche multiplication process in the collector junction is providing more majority carriers to the base than are necessary to support recombination in the base and emitter. Inasmuch as the common-emitter collector characteristics are normally shown with base current as a parameter, these curves are quite sensitive to *small amounts* of avalanche multiplication, which becomes apparent for collector voltages well below the avalanche breakdown value.

1.6.1 *Changes in the Incremental Behavior Caused by Avalanche Multiplication*

The pre-breakdown avalanche multiplication process is usually described in terms of a multiplication factor M, which is defined as the ratio of the total current crossing the junction to the primary current I_p which is produced *outside* the junction. In other words, $(M - 1)I_P$ is the current which is generated by the process of impact ionization within the junction space-charge layer.

To illustrate the effects of avalanche multiplication on the incremental behavior of a *pnp* transistor we consider a small change ΔI_P in the primary current and constrain the reverse voltage on the collector junction to be constant. Such a change in primary current can occur only if the minority-carrier flow across the base changes (by ΔI_P). In accordance with the definition of M, the rate of production of secondary hole-electron pairs generates an incremental current $(M - 1)\Delta I_P$. The increment in majority-carrier current required to support the increased recombination in the base and emitter is $\delta\Delta I_P$, where δ is the total defect. Consequently, the net increments in collector and base current are:*

$$\Delta(-I_C) = \Delta I_P + (M - 1)\Delta I_P = M\Delta I_P \qquad (1.25a)$$

$$\Delta(-I_B) = \delta\Delta I_P - (M - 1)\Delta I_P = [\delta - (M - 1)]\Delta I_P \quad (1.25b)$$

---

* In accordance with the IEEE standards, terminal currents are defined as positive *into* the device. Consequently, both I_C and I_B are negative for normal operation of a *pnp* transistor.

The apparent incremental short-circuit common-emitter current gain, which we call β_0', is thus:

$$\beta_0' = \frac{\Delta(-I_C)}{\Delta(-I_B)} = \frac{M}{\delta - (M - 1)} \qquad (1.26)$$

For low values of collector-base voltage $M \cong 1$ and $\beta_0' \cong \beta_0$ = $1/\delta$. As the collector voltage increases, $M - 1$ increases, thus increasing β_0'. At a voltage such that $M - 1 = \delta$, the apparent incremental current gain β_0' becomes infinite, and the transistor requires no increment in base current to support an increment in collector current. The collector-base voltage at which this occurs is called the *sustaining voltage* V_s.

We can estimate the sustaining voltage in terms of the avalanche breakdown voltage by employing the usual empirical relationship for the dependence of the multiplication factor M on the collector-base voltage:

$$M = \left[1 - \left(\frac{|V_{CB}|}{V_a}\right)^n\right]^{-1} \qquad (1.27)$$

in which V_a is the avalanche-breakdown voltage, and the exponent n lies in the range from 1.5 to 6.5.* The voltage at which $(M - 1)$ = δ is thus:

$$V_s = \sqrt[n]{\frac{\delta}{1 + \delta}}\, V_a \qquad (1.28)$$

For typical numerical values of δ and n, the sustaining voltage is 1/10 to 1/3 of the avalanche breakdown voltage. Inasmuch as the defect δ depends on the quiescent current at which the transistor operates, the sustaining voltage is current-dependent.† Consequently, the sustaining voltage generally appears as a contour and not as a constant-voltage line on the common-emitter collector characteristics.

If the quiescent collector-base voltage is greater than the sustaining voltage, the apparent value of β is *negative*. That is, base

---

* PEM, Sec. 4.4.1, and Ref. 1.3.
† In considering the current dependence of δ for a transistor operating at high enough collector voltages to make avalanche multiplication appreciable, it is desirable to express δ in terms of the quiescent emitter current rather than the quiescent collector current, which is itself multiplied.

current increments of a polarity opposite to that normally associated with transistor action are required to produce incremental changes in the collector current. This reversal of polarity occurs because the secondary carriers produced by the avalanche multiplication mechanism are more than adequate to support the increased recombination (see Eq. 1.25b), and the extra carriers must be removed by the base current.

The incremental output resistance of a transistor is negative for operation above the sustaining voltage. We can demonstrate the existence of this negative resistance by considering the consequences of an *increase* in the magnitude of V_{CB} for fixed I_B. Both M and I_p will change. The secondary current which flows back into the base after the increase in $|V_{CB}|$ is

$$(M + \Delta M - 1)(I_P + \Delta I_P)$$

in which M and I_P denote the multiplication factor and the primary current *before* the change. Inasmuch as the total base current is constant, the *change* in secondary current must be balanced by a change in recombination. That is,

$$(M + \Delta M - 1)(I_P + \Delta I_P) - (M - 1)I_P = \delta \Delta I_P \quad (1.29)$$

Neglecting second-order terms, and solving for the *change* in primary current yields:

$$\Delta I_P = -\frac{I_P}{(M-1) - \delta} \Delta M \quad (1.30a)$$

The corresponding *change* in the total collector current is (see Eq. 1.25a):

$$\Delta(-I_C) = (M + \Delta M)(I_P + \Delta I_P) - MI_P \quad (1.30b)$$

$$= I_P \left[1 + \frac{M}{\delta - (M-1)} \right] \Delta M$$

where we have once again neglected second-order terms. For operation above the sustaining voltage, the second term in the brackets, which is equal to the apparent current gain β_0' (see Eq. 1.26), is *negative* and large enough to dominate the expression. Furthermore, ΔM is *positive* for an increase in the magnitude of the collector-base voltage (see Eq. 1.27). Therefore, an *increase* in the magnitude of the collector-base voltage produces a *decrease* in the magnitude of the collector current, i.e., $\Delta(-I_C)$ is *negative*. The incremental output resistance for fixed base current is thus negative.

1.6.2 *Changes in the dc Output Characteristics*

The common-emitter output characteristics, in which base current is the parametric variable, are also strongly influenced by the pre-breakdown avalanche multiplication. We can understand the general nature of the collector characteristics by modifying the normal-region Ebers-Moll equations appropriately.* The primary current which crosses the collector junction can be written:

$$I_P = -\alpha_F I_E - I_{CO} \qquad (1.31a)$$

The total collector current, including the secondary current produced by impact ionization, is thus

$$I_C = -M[\alpha_F I_E + I_{co}] \qquad (1.31b)$$

Kirchoff's current law requires

$$I_B = -(I_E + I_C) \qquad (1.32)$$

If I_E is eliminated between Eqs. 1.31b and 1.32, we obtain

$$I_C = \frac{M\alpha_F}{1 - M\alpha_F} I_B - \frac{M}{1 - M\alpha_F} I_{co} \qquad (1.33)$$

This result shows that the large-signal common-emitter current gain, which is the coefficient of I_B, has a singularity when

$$M\alpha_F = 1 \qquad (1.34)$$

Since the avalanche multiplication factor M is a function of V_{CB} ($\cong V_{CE}$) and α_F is a function of the emitter current I_E ($\cong |I_C|$ if $|I_B| \ll |I_C|$), Eq. 1.34 defines a *contour* on the collector characteristics. Similarly, the zero base current curve rises to very large currents as $M\alpha_F$ approaches unity. Therefore, the collector characteristics with base current as the parameter break upward at voltages comparable to the sustaining voltage. However, it is

* PEM, Sec. 9.3.2.

important to recognize that the unbounded increase in collector current (for fixed base current) is *not* avalanche breakdown, and the transistor can be operated with collector-base voltages greater than those given by the contour of Eq. 1.34.

The features described above are illustrated in Fig. 1.21a, which shows a typical set of common-emitter output characteristics. The avalanche breakdown voltage of this transistor is about 67 volts. The sustaining voltage, at which the incremental current gain is infinite, is about 15 volts at low collector currents.

The common-emitter collector characteristics of Fig. 1.21a are quite similar, *below the sustaining voltage*, to the curves of Fig. 1.18 (which illustrate the effect of punch-through). However, a transistor can be operated with V_{CE} in excess of the *sustaining voltage*, in the region of the characteristics which correspond to reversed base current, while operation above the *punch-through voltage* is *not* possible.

The curves for reverse base current polarity change shape rather drastically for $|I_C| < I_B$, as can be seen from Fig. 1.21a. Although this region has no useful application, a word of explanation concerning the shape of the curves is in order. The negative-resistance region marked (1) in Fig. 1.21b, for reverse base current with $|I_C| > I_B$, has already been discussed. This region terminates at the point where $I_C = -I_B$, (and hence $I_E = 0$). This point lies within a few tenths of a volt of the common-base curve for $I_E = 0$, shown dotted in the figure, and hence is close to collector avalanche. Any further decrease in collector current at constant base current must cause both I_E and hence V_{EB} to go negative. That is, we now have both emitter and collector diodes reverse-biased. As pointed out in ECP, Chapter 2, there is a limiting value of emitter current possible under these conditions, which is

$$I_E = -\frac{I_{EO}(1 - \alpha_F)}{1 - \alpha_F \alpha_R}$$

a value which is unmodified by the presence of collector multiplication. This limiting value of $|I_E|$ is less than I_{EO}, (i.e., less than 1 μa, even in germanium). Thus, any attempt to make $|I_C|$ substantially smaller than I_B must force the emitter diode into avalanche, with a corresponding drop in V_{EB} to the emitter avalanche volt-

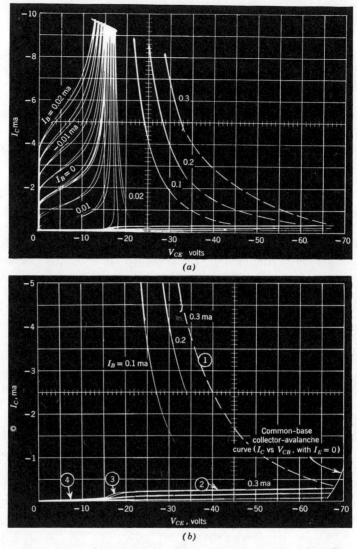

Fig. 1.21. Common-emitter output characteristics, showing the effects of avalanche multiplication and the associated reversal of base current. Punchthrough voltage for this transistor is above its avalanche voltage (heating effects cause hysteresis and abnormally large I_{C0}). (a) Oscilloscope photograph (heavy dashed lines indicate retouching). For reverse base current region, an external base current supply was used (1 megohm and 100, 200, and 300 Volts). (b) Enlarged curves for reverse base current. Techniques for measuring these characteristics are described in another volume in this series: *Handbook of Basic Transistor Circuits and Measurements* (TCM) by R. D. Thornton, et al.

age (-50 volts for this transistor). Region (*2*) in Fig. 1.21*b* thus corresponds to back bias of the emitter junction and avalanche of the collector junction. In region (*3*), both junctions are avalanched, so the associated value of V_{CE} will be close to the difference between the two avalanche voltages. Finally, in region (*4*), V_{CE} becomes small enough to drop the collector junction out of avalanche, but the emitter junction remains avalanched.

Transistors can be operated in region (*1*), often called the avalanche mode, between V_s and V_a if the circuit is arranged to accommodate the reversed base current. Because of the negative-resistance region of the collector characteristics, negative-resistance switching behavior can occur and the transistor can be used as a bistable device or as a monostable pulse generator. It is often difficult to determine the avalanche-mode collector characteristics experimentally because of oscillations associated with the negative resistance.

Operation in the avalanche-mode region of the collector characteristics may be severely limited by power dissipation in the transistor. The avalanche region occurs at relatively large values of collector voltage, and large values of collector current are possible. In addition, we should recognize that the reversal of base current which characterizes the avalanche region causes a *pinching-in* of the longitudinal current. This is in sharp contrast to the pinch-out phenomenon normally associated with high-current operation, which is discussed in Sec. 1.3. As a consequence of the crowding of collector current near the center of the collector, the local heating may be much more severe than it would be at the same total power dissipation if the collector current were uniformly distributed. Moreover, pinch-in causes the ohmic base resistance to become very large; it approaches the total resistance of the base layer, r_B, for large collector currents.

1.7 DEPENDENCE OF ELECTRICAL PARAMETERS ON OPERATING CONDITIONS

All of the parameters of the hybrid-π small-signal circuit model shown in Fig. 1.1*a* depend on the operating point of the transistor, defined by I_C and V_{CB} (or V_{CE}). We have developed the detailed physical electronics of the transistor sufficiently to permit explanation of essentially all of these parameter variations, and we now undertake that explanation.

We must emphasize that this section is intended to *supplement* and not substitute for the discussion of parameter variation presented in ECP, Chapter 4. More precisely, we do not repeat here the discussion of parameter variation which is based on the first-order physical model, but merely add to it the description of effects which can be understood only on the basis of the second-order effects which we have considered in this chapter.

The parameters on which we focus attention are the following ones.

(1) The transconductance g_m.

(2) The common-emitter short-circuit current gain β_0.

(3) The frequency f_T at which the small-signal common-emitter short-circuit current gain is unity.

(4) The small-signal base resistance r_x.

1.7.1 *The Transconductance at High Levels of Collector Current*

The incremental transconductance g_m is defined as

$$g_m \equiv - \left. \frac{\partial I_C}{\partial V_{EB'}} \right|_{V_{CB} \text{ constant}} \tag{1.35}$$

where $V_{EB'}$ is the voltage which exists between the emitter terminal and a fictitious "internal base terminal" B' which lies *inside* the base resistance. That is, $V_{EB'}$ differs from V_{EB} because it excludes ohmic drops in the base region. For collector currents small enough to insure low-level injection in the base region and large enough to allow neglect of thermal generation, the transconductance is given by Eq. 1.1:

$$g_m = \frac{q|I_C|}{kT} \tag{1.1}$$

The analysis of Sec. 1.2.3 shows that when the injection level in the base is high, the relation between I_C and $V_{EB'}$ for a *pnp* transistor is

$$I_C = -Be^{qV_{EB'}/(1+m)kT} \tag{1.36}$$

in accordance with Eq. 1.15*b*. The parameter m ranges from about

0.3 in germanium to about 0.45 in silicon. The high current trans-conductance of a *pnp* transistor is thus

$$g_m = \frac{q}{(1 + m)kT} |I_C| \qquad (1.37a)$$

The corresponding result for an *npn* transistor is

$$g_m = \frac{q}{(1 - m)kT} |I_C| \qquad (1.37b)$$

The transconductance is expressed in terms of the quiescent collector current at the operating point. Furthermore, the $g_m v$ generator in the incremental model is dependent on a voltage which lies *inside* the incremental base resistance and does not include incremental transverse ohmic drops. Consequently, high-current transconductance is *not* influenced by either the *longitudinal* electric field in the base or the pinch-out phenomenon associated with transverse "*ohmic*" voltage drops in the base. We have chosen to represent the small-signal consequences of transverse ohmic drops in terms of the incremental base resistance r_x and to represent the effects of the transverse nonohmic distributed emf in terms of the transconductance. While this choice is somewhat arbitrary, it is very convenient because it separates two basically different physical effects into two different elements in the model. While pinch out and the drift-aided transport of carriers across the base certainly influence the incremental voltage gain *of the transistor*, we model these effects in terms of changes in r_x and in r_π, respectively, rather than in terms of a modified transconductance.

1.7.2 *Common-Emitter Short-Circuit Current Gain*

This parameter is defined as

$$\beta_0 = \left.\frac{\partial I_C}{\partial I_B}\right|_{V_{CE} \text{ constant}} \qquad (1.38)$$

In terms of the parameters of the hybrid-π model its approximate value is $g_m r_\pi = 1/\delta$, where δ is the total defect of the transistor.[*] For essentially all transistors, β_0 exhibits a gradual increase with increasing collector current at low current levels followed by a

[*] PEM, Sec. 7.2.

broad maximum and a subsequent decrease as the collector current increases into the high-level injection range. Typical behavior is shown in Fig. 1.2.

Three mechanisms account for this behavior. The increase of β_0 with current at low collector currents results from the decreasing importance of incremental components of surface and space-charge layer recombination currents, as indicated in Sec. 1.1. A second factor which causes β_0 to increase as the collector current increases toward the high-level condition is the longitudinal electric field in the base, which aids the transport of minority carriers. This mechanism, which is considered in Sec. 1.2.1, is the dominant reason for increases in β_0 in germanium transistors operated under typical conditions. As we see in Fig. 1.2, the current gain peaks, and inevitably falls at very large collector currents. There are two reasons for this decrease. First, the emitter efficiency drops because of the increased injection into the emitter which occurs when the base region is in high-level injection. This mechanism is discussed in Sec. 1.2.2, where it is shown that for large enough collector currents the emitter portion of the defect becomes proportional to I_C. Second, the quasi-neutral base region widens at high collector current, as discussed in Sec. 1.5.2, thereby increasing the base portion of the defect.

The level of collector current at which the common-emitter current gain peaks corresponds roughly to the onset of high-level injection in the base. Consequently, β_0 begins to decrease at about the same value of I_C at which the transconductance changes from

$$\frac{q}{kT} |I_C| \qquad \text{to} \qquad \frac{q}{(1 \pm m)kT} |I_C| .$$

The transverse crowding of excess carriers in the base region has relatively little direct effect on the current gain. The current gain is governed by recombination mechanisms, which are more sensitive to the quantity of excess charge than to the distribution of that charge. This fact is reflected in our use of a constant lifetime for excess carriers in our analysis. The transverse crowding does make surface recombination more important, and also causes high-level injection to occur at lower collector currents. For these reasons there is some coupling between these nonlinear effects.

The common-emitter current gain is also dependent on the collector voltage. This dependence arises from collector space-charge-layer widening, which causes β_0 to increase uniformly as V_{CE} increases in magnitude as shown in Figs. 1.18c and 1.21, as well as from avalanche multiplication. The latter effect, discussed in Sec. 1.6, causes the current gain to become infinite at the sustaining voltage and to reverse sign for collector voltages greater than the sustaining voltage.

1.7.3 High-Frequency Performance — f_T

The capabilities of the transistor as a linear amplifier at very high frequencies are indicated in part by f_T, the frequency at which the magnitude of the small-signal common-emitter current gain extrapolates to unity.* In terms of the hybrid-π model with $C_{sc} = 0$, f_T is given by

$$f_T = \frac{1}{2\pi} \frac{g_m}{C_\pi + C_\mu} \qquad (1.39)$$

The parameter f_T depends on both the collector current and the collector-base voltage at the operating point. This dependence is shown for a typical silicon planar transistor in Fig. 1.22.

The dependence of f_T on V_{CE} for constant I_C results from the dependence of base width W on collector bias voltage discussed in Sec. 1.5.1. The transconductance at a given value of I_C is independent of base width. Both of the incremental capacitances in Eq. 1.39 decrease as $|V_{CE}|$ increases, thus causing f_T to increase monotonically. The base-charging component of the capacitance C_π varies as W^2 and is invariably the dominant term.†

Several physical effects combine to cause the observed dependence of f_T on I_C for constant V_{CE}. As the collector current increases from low values, a longitudinal electric field, which *aids* the flow of minority carriers across the base, develops, as shown in Sec. 1.2.1. Consequently, rapid changes in the incremental collector current can be accomplished with smaller changes in the stored excess charge; this effect appears as an increase in f_T. In

* ECP, Sec. 3.2.3.
† PEM, Sec. 7.4.

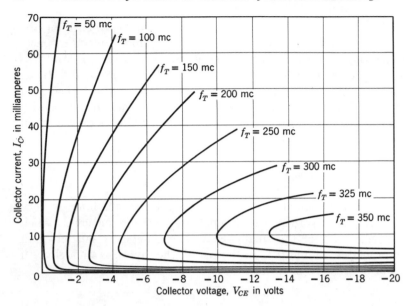

Fig. 1.22. Contours of constant f_T on the I_C-V_{CE} plane for a silicon planar transistor (Type 2N2401).

addition, in the low-current range, f_T increases with increasing collector current because g_m and the base-charging component of C_π vary as I_C while C_μ and the emitter space-charge-layer component of $C_\pi(C_{je})$ are independent of I_C. This mechanism, which alone would yield a constant high-current asymptote for f_T, is discussed in detail in ECP.* Instead of approaching a constant asymptote at high collector currents, f_T peaks and ultimately falls. This behavior occurs because of the base stretching phenomenon, treated in Sec. 1.5.2, which causes W to increase as I_C increases. Consequently, the base-charging component of C_π increases even faster than I_C, thus causing f_T to decrease.

For an important class of transistors (e.g., epitaxial and triple-diffused) the collector space-charge layer may be considerably wider than the quasi-neutral base region. For these transistors the charge associated with carriers moving through the space-charge layer has an important effect on f_T. In order to illustrate this problem, consider the idealized *pnip* transistor shown in Fig. 1.23.

* ECP, Sec. 4.1.3.

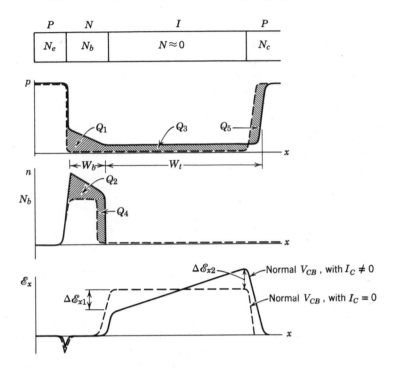

Fig. 1.23. Charge storage in the *pnip* transistor.

Here, it is assumed that the transistor is constructed with a wide intrinsic region inserted between the much lower resistivity base and collector regions. In actual transistors, the transition between the four regions may be more gradual, but the general results can be seen on this simplified model.

If a collector-base reverse bias voltage is applied to the transistor with $I_E = 0$, the plots of p, n, and $\mathcal{E}_x$ are constant in the "I" region. $\mathcal{E}_x$ falls off very quickly in the base and collector regions because of their low resistivity. When an emitter current is applied, holes flow from emitter to collector and there are changes (increments) in the charge store in the transistor. The most important of these increments are represented as shaded areas designated Q_i in Fig. 1.23. They can be identified as follows:

Q_1 is the charge associated with minority carriers diffusing between the emitter and collector space-charge layers; this is very nearly the same as for the *pnp* transistor except for the effect of the finite carrier concentration at the collector space-charge edge.

Q_2 is the majority charge which must be supplied to the base region so as to maintain charge quasi-neutrality.

Q_3 is the charge of the carriers moving through the space charge layer. Assuming that $\mathcal{E}_x$ is greater than a critical value, the carriers move through the "*i*"-region at a constant or limiting velocity, v_l, which is more or less independent of $\mathcal{E}_x$. For both germanium and silicon, v_l is on the order of 50 microns per nanosecond (i.e., 5×10^6 cm/sec, or about thermal velocity) for $\mathcal{E}_x$ greater than about 0.5 volt/micron. Thus Q_3 is given by

$$Q_3 = \frac{W_t}{v_l} I_c$$

where W_t/v_l is the time required for carriers to move through the *i*-region.

The charges Q_4 and Q_5 are the charges required to neutralize Q_3; thus $Q_4 + Q_5 = Q_3$, and $\mathcal{E}_x \simeq$ outside of the space-charge layers at each end of the *i*-region. In order to calculate the effect of Q_3 on f_T, however, we must determine what fraction of Q_3 is neutralized by the charge Q_4 in the base region. Recall that ω_T^{-1} is approximately equal to the ratio of incremental majority charge supplied by the base current to the base region, divided by the incremental collector current, with *no* increment in collector-emitter voltage (v_{CE} held constant).* Because, however, v_{BE} changes very little, ω_T^{-1} may be determined with v_{CB} held constant, which means that the area under the electric field plot in the base-collector space-charge region must remain unchanged during the increments of charge and current involved in the short-circuit current gain. Thus, under the assumption that virtually all of the collector voltage appears across the *i*-region, we must have in Fig. 1.23 $\Delta\mathcal{E}_{x1} \simeq \Delta\mathcal{E}_{x2}$, and accordingly $Q_4 \simeq Q_5$.

---

* See PEM, Eqs. 7.31 and 10.5; or ECP, Eqs. 1.15*a*, 1.21*b*, 3.37, and 4.12. Refer also to the joint Bell Telephone Laboratories, Inc. and SEEC 16mm sound color film entitled "Transistor Structure and Technology" by R. D. Thornton and J. M. Early. Distribution arrangements for SEEC films are discussed in the Foreword.

We then find:

$$Q_1 \simeq Q_2 \simeq \left(\frac{W^2{}_b}{2D_b} + \frac{W_b}{v_l} \right) I_C$$

$$Q_4 \simeq Q_5 \simeq \tfrac{1}{2} Q_3 \simeq \left(\frac{W_t}{2v_l} \right) I_C$$

where the term containing v_l in the first equation above arises because of appreciable mobile hole storage in the N-I junction space-charge layer. As a result, we find

$$\frac{1}{\omega_T} \simeq \frac{Q_2 + Q_4}{I_c} \simeq \frac{W^2{}_b}{2D_b} + \frac{W_b + \tfrac{1}{2}W_t}{v_l}$$

For a typical high-speed transistor, we might have $W_b = 0.2$ micron and $W_t = 2$ microns. Assuming $D_b = 1 (\mu m)^2/\text{nsec}$ (i.e. $D_b = 10$ cm^2/sec, which is typical of low-resistivity silicon), and $v_l = 50 \ \mu m/\text{nsec}$, we have

$$\frac{1}{\omega_T} \simeq \frac{0.22}{2} + \frac{1.2}{50} = 0.02 + 0.024 = 0.048 \ \text{nsec}$$

or

$$f_T \simeq 3.3 \ \text{gigacycles/sec}$$

Typically, emitter space-charge layer capacitances and header capacitances will reduce f_T by another factor of two; but observe that the contribution of Q_4 to f_T is at least as important as the $W_b{}^2/2D_b$ term.

Notice collaterally in Fig. 1.23 that the flow of collector current affects the peak electric field for a given collector voltage and, therefore, changes the avalanche breakdown voltage.

1.7.4 *Incremental Base Resistance*

We found in Sec. 1.3 that the effect of transverse voltage drops in the base region on the dc characteristics of the transistor *cannot*, in general, be modeled in terms of a constant lumped resistance inserted in the base lead. On the other hand, for the linear incremental model the consequences of transverse drops in the base region can be modeled in terms of a lumped impedance z_x in the base lead. Usually we represent the incremental base impedance simply as a resistance r_x, as shown in Fig. 1.1a.*

The incremental base resistance depends on both V_{CE} and I_C. The dependence on collector voltage results principally from the dependence of base width on V_{CB} discussed in Sec. 1.5.1. As the reverse-bias voltage on the collector junction increases, the collector space-charge layer widens and the base region narrows correspondingly. Inasmuch as the base current flows along the transverse dimension of the transistor, the associated voltage drops will increase as the width of the active base region through which these currents flow decreases. Consequently, the incremental base resistance increases as V_{CE} increases in magnitude.

The base resistance depends on the collector current because of the pinch-out mechanism discussed in Sec. 1.3. For very low collector currents the incremental base resistance is essentially constant, and is equal to the sum of the resistance of the inactive base region and, for a rectangular structure, one-third of the transverse resistance of the active base region. As the collector current increases, and pinch-out develops, the base resistance falls as a consequence of the modulation of the conductivity by the excess carriers and the crowding of the collector current density toward the base terminal. When pinch-out is fully developed and the base region is in high level injection, as described in Sec. 1.5.3, the active base region makes a negligible contribution to the total base resistance.

1.8 TRANSISTOR CURRENT AND VOLTAGE RATINGS

All transistors are provided by their manufacturer with certain maximum ratings. They are usually designated as "Absolute Maximum Ratings" and include specification of maximum terminal voltages and currents as well as of maximum power dissipation and temperature. We postpone discussion of power dissipation and temperature ratings until Chapter 2 and discuss here the current and voltage ratings.

---

* When r_x is added to the incremental model it is also generally necessary to split the incremental space-charge capacitance into two components. The component which is *not* charged through r_x is designated as C_{sc} (see Fig. 1.1).

1.8.1 *Collector Voltage Ratings*

The absolute maximum value of collector-base voltage at which a transistor can be operated is the lowest of either the punch-through voltage or the avalanche-breakdown voltage of the collector junction. In both cases the collector current rises without limit as V_{CE} approaches the limiting voltage, and destruction of the device by excessive internal power dissipation will occur if this high-current condition persists. The avalanche-breakdown voltage is usually designated as BV_{CBO}, which means: breakdown voltage, collector-to-base with the emitter open. The standard notation for the punch-through voltage is V_{RT} (reach-through voltage).

The transistor may also be provided with a specification of the maximum permissible collector-to-emitter voltage with the base open. This rating designates the value of the sustaining voltage and is designated as BV_{CEO}. It is, of course, not an absolute maximum rating in the same sense that BV_{CBO} is, and operation in the avalanche mode above the sustaining voltage is quite feasible. The manufacturer usually treats it as an absolute maximum rating in preparing his data sheets because operation in the avalanche mode imposes some subtle constraints on the circuit designer which, if ignored, can lead to failure of the transistor because of excessive power dissipation.*

Most data sheets also specify the avalanche breakdown voltage of the emitter junction, designated as BV_{EBO}. This rating is useful in certain switching applications in which the emitter junction of an OFF transistor may be reverse-biased by a large voltage. Many diffused transistors have emitter junction avalanche breakdown voltages as low as 2 to 5 volts because of the very heavy doping on *both* sides of the emitter junction.

1.8.2 *Collector Current Rating*

The "absolute maximum collector current" rating of a transistor is an anomaly. If the power dissipation is adequately controlled, the collector current of a transistor can be increased almost without limit. At large enough collector currents the device may

---

* Note, for example, that the temperature rise caused by internal power dissipation may be greater when there is a strong pinch-in effect because the power dissipation is quite localized. Consequently, power dissipation ratings are sometimes reduced for high voltage operation.

fail because an internal connecting wire melts. However, the currents at which this occurs may be an order of magnitude greater than the maximum value specified on the data sheet. As the collector current is increased, however, the common-emitter short circuit current gain β_0 falls toward zero, and this fact accounts for the maximum collector current rating. That is, the manufacturer specifies a maximum permissible collector current in order to enable him to also specify a lower bound for β_0. If a certain application can tolerate lower values of β_0 the transistor can safely be operated at higher currents, *provided, of course, that the power dissipation rating is not exceeded.* Note, however, that the power dissipation rating may be a function of collector current and voltage levels because of thermal instability problems, which will be discussed in Chapter 2.

REFERENCES

1.1   C.T. Sah, R. N. Noyce, and W. Shockley, "Carrier Generation and Recombination in p-n Junctions and p-n Junction Characteristics," *Proc. IRE*, **45**, 1228 (1957).

1.2   J. B. Gunn, "High Electric Field Effects in Semiconductors," *Progress in Semiconductors*, Vol. 2, 1957.

1.3   S. L. Miller, "Avalanche Breakdown in Ge," *Phys. Rev.*, **99**, 1234 (1955).

PROBLEMS

P1.1   Junction diodes intended for use with large reverse voltages are usually fabricated with a wide near-intrinsic region between the heavily doped p-type and n-type regions. The near-intrinsic region can support a large reverse voltage while keeping the electric field small enough to avoid avalanche multiplication. These structures are often called p-i-n diodes. Consider the p-i-n structure shown in Fig. 1.24a. The corresponding impurity distribution is shown in Fig. 1.24b.

(a) Calculate the static IV characteristic of the diode. That is, find $I = I(V)$. The following assumptions should be made:

(1) All of the applied voltage appears as changes in the heights of the potential barriers at the two junctions.

(2) Injected excess carriers move in the intrinsic region solely by diffusion, and the diffusion length L is *much greater* than the width W of the intrinsic region. The diffusion constant is D.

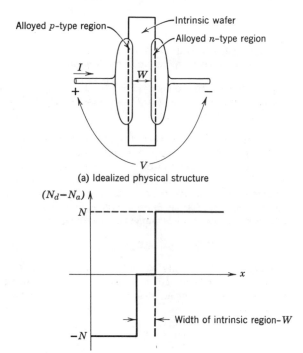

(a) Idealized physical structure

(b) Impurity distribution

Fig. 1.24. p-i-n Junction diode.

(3) The impurity concentration N of the alloyed regions is much greater than n_i.

(b) When this diode is forward-biased, holes are injected into the i-region from the p-type region and electrons are injected into the i-region from the n-type side. What happens to these injected excess carriers? Discuss briefly the relevance of the p-i-n forward IV characteristic to the low-current behavior of β_0 discussed in Sec. 1.1.

P1.2 The analysis, in Sec. 1.2.1, of the effects of high level injection on minority carrier transport in the base relies on the assumption that quasi-neutrality holds in the base; i.e., the total space charge is negligible compared with its positive or negative constituents.

(a) Use Gauss' law and Eq. 1.2 to determine the net space charge $\rho(x)$ (note that dp_b/dx is *not* independent of x in high level injection inasmuch as J_{hx} *must* be independent of x because recombination in the base has a negligible effect on J_{hx}).

(b) Consider an alloy transistor in which $n_{bo} = 2 \times 10^{15}$ cm^{-3}, $W = 5 \times 10^{-4}$ cm, and $D_b = 50$ cm^2/sec. Determine the approximate value of collector current density at which $\rho(W) = 0.1qn_{bo}$. What is the corresponding value of $p_b(0)/n_{bo}$?

P1.3   Express the emitter defect, given by Eq. 1.8, in terms of the dc collector current of the transistor. Assume space-charge neutrality in the base region.

P1.4   The equations which govern the low-level-injection transverse distribution of voltage in the base region of a transistor having *rectangular* geometry are developed in Sec. 1.3.2 (see Eq. 1.17). Develop the corresponding equations for a transistor having *cylindrical* geometry. Assume that the active region is a right circular cylinder of radius r_o and of height W, having a resistivity ρ, and that the base contact is cylindrical and surrounds the entire active region.

P1.5   Derive Eq. 1.24b from Eq. 1.24a.

P1.6   Use Eq. 1.21 to evaluate the *total* collector current I_C. Show that if the base and collector currents are small enough so that negligible crowding exists (γh small) the total collector current can be written in the form

$$I_C = I_o e^{q(V_0 - R_B I_{B0})/kT}$$

where I_0 is a constant and R_B is the *dc base resistance*. Prove that $R_B = r_B/3$, where r_B is the transverse resistance of the active base region. (See also PEM, P8.4.)

P1.7   Employ the analysis of Sec. 1.6.1 to derive an expression for the incremental output resistance r_o of a *pnp* transistor operated in the common-emitter connection. Sketch the dependence of r_o on $|V_{CE}|$ for fixed *emitter current*.

P1.8   As illustrated in Fig. 1.16, an epitaxial transistor structure employs a thin layer of high-resistivity collector material which is grown on a much thicker low-resistivity substrate. Why is this high-resistivity epitaxial layer necessary? In other words, why are not the transistors diffused directly into the low-resistivity substrate?

P1.9   An alloy-junction *pnp* germanium transistor has a nominal metallurgical base width of 4×10^{-4} cm and a nominal base resistivity of 0.5 ohm-cm. The impurity concentration in the emitter and collector is greater than 10^{18} cm^{-3}.
(a) Estimate the punch-through voltage.
(b) Estimate the actual base width at a collector-base voltage of one-half the punch-through voltage.

P1.10 When the transistor whose collector characteristics are shown in Fig. 1.21 is used in the circuit of Fig. 1.25a, it exhibits the driving-point characteristic shown in Fig. 1.25b. Explain the principal features of this curve.

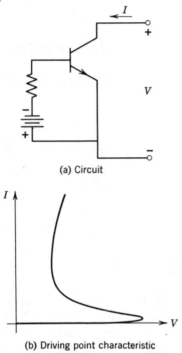

(a) Circuit

(b) Driving point characteristic

Fig. 1.25. Avalanche-mode operation.

2

Temperature and Power Limitations of Transistors

2.0 INTRODUCTION

Most transistor applications involve thermal considerations. For example, it may be necessary to limit the variation of certain circuit parameters over a range of environmental temperatures, to preserve operating point stability at high ambient temperature, or to dissipate relatively high power in the transistor without degrading its characteristics. In this chapter we investigate the following two aspects of the temperature-dependence of the electrical characteristics of transistors.

(1) Ambient temperature limitations and power dissipation limitations.

(2) Thermal instabilities.

We do not consider in detail the sources of temperature dependence of the dc characteristics and of the small-signal parameters, because these topics are explored sufficiently in PEM and ECP.*

* PEM, Secs. 3.3.4 and 9.1.3; ECP, Sec. 4.3.

2.1 TEMPERATURE AND POWER DISSIPATION LIMITATIONS

Most transistors are supplied by their manufacturers with several temperature and power ratings. For example, there are usually prescribed upper and lower limits for the allowable range of storage temperatures; an upper, and sometimes a lower, limit for the operating temperature of the junctions; and a maximum power dissipation specification. We now examine these limitations in some detail, and explore the relationships between them.

2.1.1 *Storage-Temperature Limitations*

The minimum storage temperature for a junction device usually ranges from -50 to $-75°C$. This limit is established to avoid mechanical damage to the transistor caused by strains associated with differential thermal contraction. All transistor structures contain broad-area joints between metals and semiconductors which may have quite different thermal expansion coefficients. For example, in alloy-junction transistors the aluminum or indium emitter and collector dots are bonded to the recrystallized portions of the semiconductor base wafer. In diffused structures the collector body is frequently soldered to the metal header, and the metallic emitter and base contacts are evaporated onto the semiconductor. Temperature excursions must be limited to avoid the possibility of fracturing these joints. Because the joints are usually fabricated at elevated temperatures, differential thermal expansion imposes a limit only at low temperatures.

The maximum storage temperature, which ranges from 85 to $120°C$ for germanium devices and to as much as $300°C$ for some silicon devices, involves two considerations:

(1) The temperature of the device must remain below that at which solders soften or alloying metals melt.

(2) The chemical activity of contaminants increases at elevated temperatures. Consequently the electrical parameters of the transistor may be unstable at high temperatures, and deleterious aging effects may be accelerated. The exposed edges of the transistor junctions are particularly sensitive to contaminants. For this reason, methods of protecting the surfaces with oxide layers have become widely used in transistor fabrication (e.g. "planar" technology).

2.1.2 *Operating-Temperature Limitations*

Transistor action can be obtained in conventional structures for temperatures as low as the boiling point of liquid nitrogen ($-196°C$). As the temperature falls even lower, into the cryogenic region, carrier concentrations decrease as the electrical impurities become only partially ionized, and the electrical behavior of the transistor changes markedly. However, the manufacturer invariably specifies a minimum operating temperature which is well above that at which carriers "freeze out" in significant quantities. The structural factors discussed in Sec. 2.1.1 obviously require that the minimum operating-temperature rating be no less than the minimum storage-temperature rating. In some cases the manufacturer sets the operating limit higher, in order to narrow the range within which he guarantees the values of the electrical parameters of the device.

The maximum operating temperature is often less than the maximum storage temperature discussed in Sec. 2.1.1. It ranges from 85°C in some germanium transistors to as high as 200°C in certain silicon units. To the extent that the maximum operating-temperature rating is less than the maximum storage-temperature rating, it is set by reversible changes in electrical performance which occur at high temperatures. These changes are usually tied to the extraordinary temperature dependence of the equilibrium minority carrier concentrations.* At high enough temperatures, all of the semiconductor regions approach intrinsic conditions, and the junctions lose their distinguishing features.

It is important to recognize that the maximum operating-temperature specification refers to the temperature *in the active region* of the transistor. Because most of the power dissipation occurs at the collector junction, the temperature of the active region is greater than the temperature of the header and case, or of the environment.

2.1.3 *Power-Dissipation Ratings and Thermal Resistance*

As the power dissipated in a transistor increases, the temperature of the active region increases.† The maximum permissible

---

* See, for example, ISP, Sec. 3.5.

† The internal temperature of the transistor is usually called the *junction temperature* or the *collector junction temperature*. The base region is thin enough so that the active region is essentially isothermal in the longitudinal direction.

value of the power dissipation corresponds to an active-region temperature which is just equal to the specified maximum operating temperature. Inasmuch as the internal temperature depends on the ambient temperature, a power-dissipation rating is meaningless unless the corresponding ambient temperature is specified.

In essentially all transistors the heat flow out of the active region is proportional to the temperature difference between the active region and the case or header. There are two reasons for this simple proportionality. First, the internal temperature differences are small enough so that heat flows internally by *conduction* only. Second, the thermal conductivity of each of the materials in the internal heat-flow path, including the semiconductor and the other structural parts, is not significantly temperature-dependent over the range of temperatures encountered in normal device operation.

As a consequence of the proportionality between heat flow and internal temperature difference, the junction temperature, which we designate as T_j, is linearly related to both the case or header temperature T_c and the internal power dissipation P.

$$T_j = T_c + \theta_i P \tag{2.1}$$

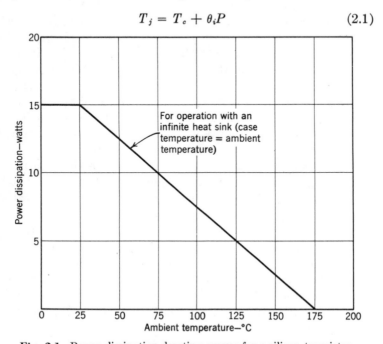

Fig. 2.1. Power dissipation derating curves for a silicon transistor.

The parameter θ_i in Eq. 2.1, above, is called the *internal thermal resistance*. It may be as small as 0.2°C/watt in a power transistor or as large as 100°C/watt in a transistor intended for low-power applications. If the value of the thermal resistance is not given explicitly by the manufacturer, it can usually be inferred from the maximum power dissipation rating; when the transistor dissipates the maximum rated power (for a particular ambient temperature) the junction is at the specified maximum operating temperature.

The static thermal rating of a transistor is occasionally presented in terms of a *derating curve*, shown in Fig. 2.1. The internal thermal resistance can, of course, be inferred from this curve. The transistor whose derating curve is shown in Fig. 2.1 has $\theta_i = 10$°C/watt. Most derating curves are flat below an ambient temperature of 25°C, as in Fig. 2.1, rather than showing further increases of the maximum rated power dissipation for lower ambient temperatures. This convention reflects the fact that transistors are seldom operated at lower ambient temperatures, as well as the manufacturer's desire to limit the internal temperature differential with which the transistor will be operated.

The internal thermal resistance provides a basis for relating the junction temperature and the case temperature to the power dissipation, as shown by Eq. 2.1. However, in all practical situations, the case temperature is itself dependent upon the power dissipation, as well as upon the ambient temperature. That is, the heat evolved inside the transistor must be removed by a *heat sink*, and the temperature of the heat sink T_s must, perforce, be greater than the temperature of the surroundings, the ambient temperature, because the heat sink itself merely transfers heat to the surroundings.

Most heat sinks transfer the heat evolved in the transistor to the surroundings by some combination of conduction, convection, and radiation. Furthermore, the temperature rise of the heat sink above ambient is, in general, a nonlinear function of the power dissipation. In many practical situations, however, the temperature rise is small enough so that a linear approximation is sufficiently accurate. Such a linear model reduces the thermal properties of the heat sink to a single number—the *thermal resistance θ_s of the heat sink*. The corresponding linear relationship between heat-sink temperature T_s, ambient temperature T_a, and power dissipation P is

$$T_s = T_a + \theta_s P \qquad (2.2)$$

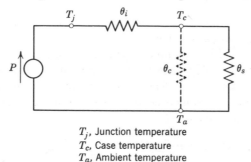

T_j, Junction temperature
T_c, Case temperature
T_a, Ambient temperature

Fig. 2.2. Lumped model for the static thermal characteristics of a transistor and heat sink. θ_c represents the heat loss from the transistor case to the ambient. Unless the transistor is operated *without* a separate heat sink, the heat removal mechanism represented by θ_c is usually included in θ_s.

Consequently, the relationship between junction temperature, ambient temperature, and power dissipation is, from Eqs. 2.1 and 2.2, with $T_c = T_s$,

$$T_j = T_a + (\theta_i + \theta_s)P \tag{2.3}$$

In other words, the total thermal resistance between the junctions and the ambient is the sum of the thermal resistances of the transistor and heat sink.*

The thermal properties of a transistor and heat sink can be represented by a lumped electric circuit model which is an analog for the temperature-power relationships. Such a model is shown in Fig. 2.2. *Voltages* in the model are analogous to *temperature* and are labeled accordingly. *Currents* in the model are analogous to *heat flow,* and the electrical resistances shown are analogs of the various thermal resistances.

Transistors intended for use with an external dissipator or heat sink are usually specified in terms of either an *internal* thermal resistance or, equivalently, a maximum power-dissipation rating for a specified *case temperature.* On the other hand, transistors

---

* In obtaining Eq. 2.3 we have simply assumed that the case temperature is equal to the heat-sink temperature. In many power transistor applications it is necessary to account for the temperature difference between the case or header and the heat sink. Such temperature rise across the mounting interface can be accounted for in terms of an additional thermal resistance which may be comparable to θ_i. Furthermore, we have included heat flow directly from the case or header to the environment (by radiation and convection) in the thermal resistance of the heat sink.

intended for low-power applications are often operated without heat sinks or dissipators. Heat is removed by natural convection from the case and by conduction through the leads. Such devices are commonly specified in terms of a maximum power-dissipation rating for a particular *ambient* temperature. The corresponding over-all thermal resistance is, of course, much greater than the internal thermal resistance.

2.1.4 *Dynamic Power-Dissipation Ratings*

The discussion of the previous section is limited to static conditions in which the transistor power dissipation and temperatures are not changing with time. In many applications the power dissipation changes with time, thereby causing the junction temperature, and perhaps also the case temperature, to have time-varying components. In general, the simple calculations of the previous section and the lumped models shown in Fig. 2.1 are not applicable under dynamic conditions. Changing temperatures are associated with changes in the internal stored energy represented by the specific heats of the semiconductor material and of the header and other structural parts. The associated heat flows may be comparable to or larger than the heat flow described by the thermal resistance.

A reasonably accurate description of the temperature distribution within the transistor under dynamic conditions can be obtained only if the distributed nature of the thermal system is accounted for. More precisely, the transient thermal behavior is governed by a partial differential equation in which the specific heat and the thermal conductivity of the semiconductor appear. Although solutions of this differential equation, which can usually be regarded as one-dimensional, are easily obtained, they are transcendental in nature and are awkward to use and interpret. Rather than considering the distributed thermal problem in detail, we focus on two important limiting situations which can be understood on intuitive grounds.

The first limiting situation obtains when changes in internal power dissipation occur extremely rapidly. Such is usually the case in switching applications as well as in linear or quasi-linear rf amplifiers. In these cases the power dissipation changes occur in a few nanoseconds or, at most, in microseconds, and the temperature distribution within the transistor remains essentially constant as a consequence of the "*thermal mass*" (or thermal capacitance) of the material. The temperature at the junction is related to the case temperature and to the *time-average* power dissipation through the *static* thermal resistance in accordance with Eq. 2.1. The difference between the instantaneous power dissipation and the corresponding time-average value is absorbed in the thermal mass of the structure as a change in stored energy. The associated temperature changes are negligibly small because the power changes occur extremely rapidly.

If the changes in power dissipation occur much more slowly, on a time scale of milliseconds or slower, the thermal behavior of the transistor can be characterized in an approximate manner by a lumped dynamic model, in which the heat flow associated with changing temperatures is represented by lumped thermal capacitances. The simplest possible lumped dynamic model is shown in Fig. 2.3a. Normally the internal thermal capacitance C_i is several orders of magnitude smaller than the thermal capacitance of the heat sink C_s. Consequently, the immediate response of the junction temperature to a step change in power dissipation is approximately exponential with a time constant of $C_i\theta_i$. This single-lump model of the transistor becomes inaccurate for times less than this time constant. Analysis of the distributed thermal system shows that, initially, the temperature rises much faster than the exponential, as indicated in Fig. 2.3b. If the single-lump model is used to predict the temperature rise produced by a pulse of power dissipation, the duration of which is short compared with the thermal time constant, the model will err on the low side. That is, the actual peak transient junction temperature may be considerably greater than that which is predicted by the model.

The lumped thermal model can, of course, be made more accurate for rapid transients by using more RC sections to represent the distributed thermal system inside the transistor case. Such a multiple-lump model is shown in Fig. 2.3c.

2.2 THERMAL INSTABILITIES

Under certain operating conditions the junction operating temperature and the power dissipation of a transistor can become

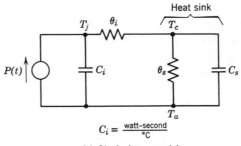

$$C_i = \frac{\text{watt-second}}{{}^\circ C}$$

(a) Single-lump model
for the transistor

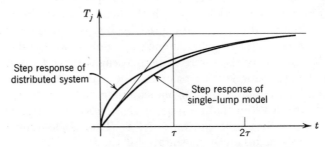

(b) Response of junction temperature for
a step change in power dissipation

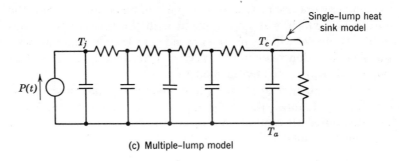

(c) Multiple-lump model

Fig. 2.3. Lumped thermal models for use in transient calculations for short times.

unstable, in the sense that both increase without apparent limit until the transistor is destroyed. This unstable condition, which manifests itself at the terminals as a rapid, unbounded increase in collector current which persists until failure occurs, is referred to as *thermal runaway*. In addition, transistors can exhibit an *internal* thermal instability which causes the minority carrier current across the base to crowd into one small portion of the active region. As a consequence of this current crowding, a hot spot develops. This mechanism of thermal instability is even more insidious than simple thermal runaway because it may cause only subtle changes in the terminal characteristics, and thus may go undetected until a transient overload condition causes device failure. If the temperature rise of the hot spot is great enough, a discontinuous change in the electrical characteristics of the transistor can occur, apparently because of local melting of the semiconductor.

2.2.1 *Thermal Runaway*

Thermal runaway occurs because the dc collector current of a transistor increases as the junction temperature increases. There are several sources of this positive temperature coefficient of I_C:*

(1) I_{CO}, which is a component of I_C, increases exponentially with temperature at a rate of about 10 to 16% per °C.

(2) If the base current is constrained by the circuit to be constant, the collector current increases with temperature because the dc common-emitter current gain increases with temperature.

(3) If the emitter-base voltage is constrained by the circuit to be constant, the emitter current, and thus the collector current, increases exponentially with temperature at a rate of about 8% per °C.

In circuits using germanium transistors, the exponential increase of I_{CO} with temperature is the principal reason for the increase of I_C with increasing temperature. Silicon transistors generally have negligibly small values of I_{CO} except at very high operating temperatures. Therefore, thermal runaway occurs less frequently in circuits using silicon transistors; when it does occur, it usually results from the strong temperature dependence of the emitter current in circuits which constrain the emitter-base voltage to be nearly constant.

* See, for example, PEM, Sec. 3.3.4, and ECP, Sec. 5.3.

Often the dc power dissipation increases with increasing collector current and thus with increasing junction temperature. The increased power dissipation must be removed by increased heat conduction, which requires a further increase in junction temperature. If the rate of increase of power dissipation with respect to junction temperature exceeds the rate of increase of heat flow through the thermal resistance for all safe temperatures, an equilibrium temperature does not exist, and the junction temperature increases without limit until something melts. From a feedback point of view, the dependence of collector current on junction temperature introduces positive feedback into the thermal system, and thermal runaway occurs when the loop gain exceeds unity.

The dependence of power dissipation on junction temperature can be inferred from the locus of operating points in the V_{CB}-I_C plane, as shown in Fig. 2.4a.* The collector current invariably increases in magnitude as the junction temperature increases. Consequently, a set of operating points for equal increments of junction temperature might be distributed along the dc load line as shown in Fig. 2.4a. The corresponding dependence of power dissipation on junction temperature is shown in Fig. 2.4b.

The internally-generated heat must be removed by conduction through the transistor structure and must be dissipated in the environment by the heat sink. The rate at which heat can thus be removed depends linearly on the junction temperature, as shown by Eq. 2.3. Consequently the curve which describes the rate of heat removal from the active region is a straight line on the coordinates of Fig. 2.4b, as shown by the line labeled AA'. This line intersects the line corresponding to $P = 0$ at $T_j = T_a$, the ambient temperature, and has a slope of $(\theta_i + \theta_s)^{-1}$. For the situation depicted by the line AA' there are three points of equilibrium at which the rate of heat generation equals the rate of heat removal. By considering the effect of a small deviation from equilibrium, we can easily show that points a and b are *stable* while point c is *unstable*. That is, a disturbance away from point a or point b establishes a thermal imbalance which tends to return the system to the original equilibrium point. On the other hand, any disturbance away from point c is augmented by the resulting imbalance.

---

* Inasmuch as $V_{CE} \cong V_{CB}$ in the normal region of operation of a transistor, these contours are essentially the same in the V_{CE}-I_C plane.

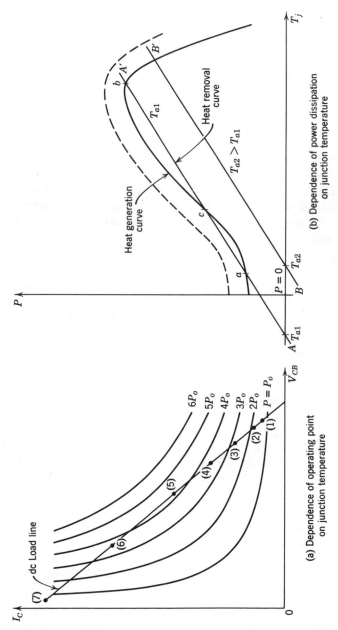

Fig. 2.4. Illustrating the dependence of operating point and power dissipation on junction temperature. The points (*1*), (*2*), ..., (*6*) denote operating points for equal temperature increments.

Although points a and b are both stable, the junction temperature which corresponds to point b may be so high that the transistor burns out before reaching point b. Clearly small values of dc load resistance, which correspond to nearly vertical load lines, cause this stable equilibrium point to shift to very high temperatures. In such cases, the thermal system appears to have only one stable operating condition, point a, because burn-out occurs well below point b. Even if the junction temperature at point b is within the temperature rating of the transistor, operation at point b is usually undesirable. The circuit is usually biased properly for operation at the low-temperature equilibrium point, so that the electrical operating point which corresponds to b is usually unsatisfactory. Nevertheless, we consider the transistor and circuit represented by the solid heat generation curve and the heat removal curve AA' to be *stable* because the system will settle at point a when power is applied.

Consider, however, the consequences of an increase in ambient temperature. The heat generation curve is unchanged while the heat removal curve is translated to the right, as shown by the line BB'. In this case only one high-temperature point of intersection exists. If the junction temperature at that point is greater than the temperature at which burn-out occurs, the apparently-unbounded increase of junction temperature which begins when power is applied terminates with transistor failure. This condition is known as *thermal runaway*.

A transistor circuit, which had been thermally stable, can develop thermal instability in several ways. An increase in the collector supply voltage, or the removal of the signal from a linear (Class A) power amplifier, can cause the entire heat-generation curve to shift upward, as shown by the dotted line in Fig. 2.4b. An increase in ambient temperature, or an increase in the thermal resistance of a heat sink (such as might be caused by the obstruction of air flow over a convection heat sink) can shift the heat-removal curve downward and to the right. Either change can produce a situation in which the curves intersect only at high temperatures, in which case the transistor may be destroyed by excessive power dissipation.*

* Several analytical techniques have been developed to facilitate evaluation of the conditions required for *tangency* of the two curves. See, for example, page 107, Ref. 2.1.

Thermal runaway can also be triggered by a more subtle mechanism which involves transient disturbances in power dissipation. Consider a situation described by the solid heat-generation curve and the heat-removal curve AA' in Fig. 2.4b. Assume that a brief electrical disturbance causes the heat generation to increase to that described by the dotted curve for a short time, after which it decreases to its former value. Obviously, the junction temperature increases during the transient disturbance because the rate of heat generation exceeds the rate of heat removal. If T_j is in excess of the temperature of the *unstable* intersection at the end of the transient increase in power dissipation, *the temperature will continue to rise*, and the junction temperature will tend toward point b, which may result in destruction of the transistor. The temperature difference between the two lower points of equilibrium can therefore be regarded as a crude margin of stability. If this margin is too small, a transient disturbance can cause an apparently stable situation to become unstable.

2.2.2 *Internal Thermal Runaway and Hot Spot Development*

In most modern transistor structures the thermal resistance from one small portion of the active region to some other portion may be comparable to the thermal resistance from either portion to the case or header. It follows that significant *transverse* temperature gradients can exist across the active region under appropriate conditions. These transverse temperature differences can lead to a thermal instability because of an internal positive feedback mechanism somewhat similar to the temperature dependence of the collector current which gives rise to thermal runaway.

Consider a transistor in which the ohmic voltage drops in the base region are small enough so that the change with applied voltage in the height of the emitter potential barrier is *uniform* across the transverse dimension. If the active region is isothermal, the longitudinal current density of minority carriers is likewise uniform. However, if the temperature in one portion of the active region increases above that of the rest of the region, there is an increase of the equilibrium minority-carrier concentration, and thus also of the minority-carrier current density in that portion of the active region. This increase in collector-current density produces an increase in the local power dissipation, which requires a further increase in local temperature, and so forth. The result is a nonuniform transverse distribution of both temperature and collector-current density, with the hottest portions carrying the most current.

In most applications of transistors, the dc circuit is designed to constrain not the emitter-base voltage but the total emitter or collector current. The circuit is designed in this manner in part to prevent gross thermal instability of the type discussed in Sec. 2.2.1. Nevertheless, nonuniform transverse distributions of current and temperature can arise. An increase in local temperature causes the emitter-base voltage to decrease in order to avoid an increase in total current. Consequently, the current density in the cooler portions of the active region decreases while the total collector current remains essentially constant. Once again the transverse distribution of collector current density may be quite nonuniform, with most of the current carried by the hot spots.

Under certain conditions the positive feedback mechanism discussed above may lead to an unstable situation in which all of the collector current crowds into small portions of the active region, which may then become extremely hot. Experiments with temperature-sensitive paint demonstrate that the temperature of the hot spot may be as high as 400°C.* Under these extreme conditions the cooler portions of the transistor are essentially cut off.

The mode of internal thermal instability which leads to hot-spot development is different from the over-all thermal instability known as thermal runaway in the following two significant ways.

(1) Hot spots can develop for *any value* of external load resistance. Transverse instability is not strongly dependent on the *external* conditions and involves primarily the nonuniform redistribution of the same total collector current.

(2) Until the hot-spot temperature reaches destructive values, it is difficult to detect, at the terminals, the presence of an internal instability. The only telltale sign is a marked reduction in emitter-base voltage when the hot spot develops.

It appears that lateral thermal instability can occur in all types of transistor structures if the internal temperature is high enough. Hot-spot development is probably a fundamental limitation on

* See References 2.2 and 2.3.

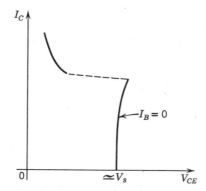

Fig. 2.5. Second breakdown in a transistor with no base current.

transistor performance and not just an unfortunate attribute of a poorly-designed or defective device.

This is a particularly serious problem in high-frequency power transistors which necessarily have narrow base regions and large emitter peripheries. There are then high thermal and electrical resistances between various sections of the active base region and the current sharing problem is similar to that faced in the use of parallel connections of discrete transistors. In fact, one method of minimizing thermal instabilities is to build the transistor with a distributed series emitter resistance analogous to the emitter resistors normally used when paralleling a number of discrete transistors.

If the total power dissipation of the transistor is large enough, and if a hot spot develops, the local temperature of the active region can reach the melting point of the semiconductor.* When melting occurs the electrical conductivity of the local molten region increases discontinuously by almost two orders of magnitude, and the collector voltage drops abruptly, as shown in Fig. 2.5. This phenomenon may be reversible, or it may cause the transistor to fail. In those cases where failure does not occur, the electrical characteristics of the transistor usually undergo a significant permanent change. A transistor which fails in this mode usually exhibits a direct short between emitter and collector. Microscopic examination of units which have failed in this manner usually reveals

* Germanium melts at 936°C, silicon at 1420°C.

minute recrystallized regions which bridge the base layer, thus lending support to the hypothesis that local melting occurs.

Discontinuities in transistor collector characteristics such as those illustrated in Fig. 2.5 were observed prior to the direct observation of hot-spot development.* This behavior has been called *second breakdown* or *secondary breakdown*. Although lateral thermal instability and hot-spot development are responsible for some of the behavior called second breakdown, there may be other non-thermal mechanisms which cause similar changes in *I-V* characteristics. For example, the reduction of the avalanche-breakdown voltage, which occurs in some devices at high collector currents and which is associated with base stretching (see Sec. 1.5.2), may produce a very-high-speed regenerative effect which causes the behavior described as second breakdown.

Probably the most important effect of thermal instabilities is to reduce the allowable power dissipation below the values that would be expected on the basis of average thermal resistance and junction temperature limitations. For example, at low collector currents and high collector voltages there is more tendency for local hot spots to form and hence *local* temperature may be greatly in excess of the average temperature. This effect may be included in circuit calculations by considering the thermal resistance to be a function of collector voltage and current. For example, one silicon power transistor is rated at $\theta_i = 0.75°C/watt$ at high currents and low voltages but is rated $\theta_i = 2°C/watt$ at low currents and high voltages. Note, however, that this does not mean that there is a significant change in the actual thermal conductivity within the transistor, but only that the power dissipation is more non-uniform in one case than in the other. Hence, the curves in the $I_C - V_{CE}$ plane which define the maximum power dissipation are not constant-power hyperbolas.

REFERENCES

2.1   *General Electric Transistor Manual*, 7th Edition, 1964.

2.2   R. M. Scarlett, W. Shockley, R. H. Haitz, "Thermal Instabilities and Hot Spots in Junction Transistors," *Physics of Failure in Electronics*, Spartan Books, Inc., Baltimore, 1963.

* See References 2.4 and 2.5.

2.3   R. M. Scarlett and W. Shockley, "Secondary Breakdown and Hot Spots in Power Transistors," *IEEE Convention Record*, pt. 3, 3–13, 1963.

2.4   H. A. Schafft and J. C. French, "Second Breakdown in Transistors," *IRE Transactions on Electron Devices*, ED 9, 129–136 (1962).

2.5   A. C. English, "Mesoplasmas and Second Breakdown in Silicon Junctions," *Solid-State Electronics*, **6**, 511–521 (1963).

PROBLEMS

P2.1   A certain silicon low-power transistor has the following thermal ratings:

Maximum junction temperature — 200°C.

Maximum power dissipation for a case temperature of 25°C — 1 watt.

Maximum power dissipation for operation in free air at 25°C ambient — 200 mw.

(a) What is the internal thermal resistance?

(b) What is the maximum permissible power dissipation for a case temperature of 75°C?

(c) For operation in free air, what is the thermal resistance between the case and ambient?

(d) What is the maximum permissible power dissipation for operation in free air at 100°C?

P2.2   A germanium power transistor has a guaranteed maximum thermal resistance between junction and case of 0.5°C/watt. The maximum junction temperature rating is 100°C.

(a) This transistor is designated as a "150-watt" unit. Under what conditions can it be safely operated with 150-watt dissipation?

(b) A natural convection heat sink having about 250 sq in. of surface and occupying about 50 cu in. of space can dissipate about 50 watts for a 50°C rise above ambient. Determine the maximum permissible power dissipation of the power transistor mounted on this heat sink in a 50°C ambient. Assume that the thermal resistance between transistor case and heat sink is 0.3°C/watt.

P2.3   The transistor shown in Fig. 2.6 (p. 84) is biased with constant base current. The collector current has two terms: a constant component of 5 ma, and a temperature-dependent component which has the value of 100 μa at a junction temperature of 25°C, and which doubles for every 10°C increase in junction temperature. The internal thermal resistance is 100°C/watt.

(a) Assume the case temperature is fixed at 25°C. What is the maximum value of V_{CC} for which the system is thermally stable?

(b) If $V_{CC} = 40$ v, what is the junction temperature?

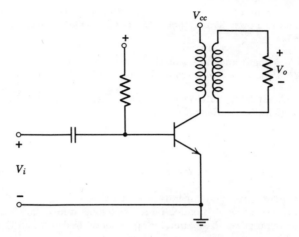

Fig. 2.6. Transistor power amplifier.

3

Speed Limitations

3.0 INTRODUCTION

The speed with which a circuit can respond is determined by the circuit configuration as well as the number and type of transistors and passive components in the circuit. Inevitably, however, regardless of the choice of circuit configuration and passive components, there are unavoidable speed limitations which depend on the transistor characteristics. If one attempts to design an amplifier with specific impedance or gain characteristics, for example a flat low-pass response with a monotonic cutoff, it is important to know whether the main prescribed features, such as the low frequency gain and the upper half-power frequency, are compatible with the properties of available transistors. The objective of this chapter is to develop methods of assessing the range of frequency-response or transient-response performance which can be obtained from a given transistor, independent, to a large extent, of the detailed circuit-element configurations employed with it.

The approach is to consider first the gain-bandwidth limitations of a common-emitter small-signal amplifier, then the more general maximum frequency-of-oscillation limitations, and finally some large-signal limitations on rate of change of voltage and current.

3.1 SOME COMMON-EMITTER GAIN-BANDWIDTH LIMITATIONS

Most of this section is concerned with predicting gain and speed limitations for the single-stage common-emitter amplifier configuration shown in Fig. 3.1. Here N_1 and N_2 are restricted to be three-terminal coupling networks constructed from positive-value R, L, and C components, or their equivalents, without any transformers. Otherwise, these networks are unrestricted. The transistor is assumed to be linear and described by the four *common-emitter* y-parameters y_i, y_r, y_f, and y_o; for convenience we shall drop the subscript e normally used to specify common-emitter parameters. The biasing network is not specifically shown in Fig. 3.1, but any passive admittances used for biasing are presumed to be part of N_1 and N_2. Y_L is assumed to be passive and signal levels are assumed to be small enough to make linear analysis valid.

We now undertake the task of finding limitations on the realizable response of this common-emitter configuration. Our interest is not on the actual design of N_1 and N_2 but, rather, on calculations of limitations which cannot be avoided for any choice of N_1 and N_2 within the general restrictions described above. Unfortunately, the exact solution of this problem appears to be difficult, and has never been carried out (except for a few special cases wherein the nature of the y-parameters is restricted). However, if we are willing to settle for *necessary* instead of *sufficient* conditions for realizability, we can derive some very simple constraints. The reasonableness of these constraints must then be checked by consideration of important special cases.

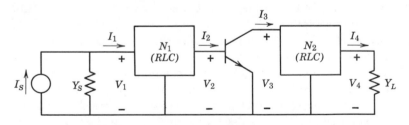

Fig. 3.1. Single-stage common-emitter amplifier. N_1 and N_2 are transformerless, passive networks.

3.1.1 *Current Gain*

To appreciate the difficulties of describing in great generality the gain and speed capabilities of the circuit of Fig. 3.1, if N_1 and N_2 were really unrestricted, note the following. If N_1 were completely arbitrary, and a step of current were applied at the input with the system initially at rest, the base current could reach values substantially greater than the input current (consider the use of a high Q tuned circuit). In fact, the total charge supplied to the transistor base could exceed the charge supplied at the input. Thus, it is not immediately clear to what extent the current gain of the transistor itself implies any limits on the current gain of the whole amplifier. Intuition and experiment both suggest that β_0 and ω_T do, in fact, imply limitations on over-all current gain, but the limit is not, in general, easily expressible in terms of time response or frequency response for $s = j\omega$. For example, in the most general case the ac current gain *can* greatly exceed β_0, and the product of current gain times frequency *can* greatly exceed ω_T.

Consider, first, therefore, some of the limitations on the realizable current gain of the special class of three-terminal transformerless *RLC* networks, terminated in passive loads. In particular, note that for the circuit of Fig. 3.2 the current gain I_2/I_1 can be written as

$$\frac{I_2}{I_1}(s) = \frac{P(s)}{Q(s)} = \frac{a_0 + a_1 s + a_2 s^2 + \dots}{b_0 + b_1 s + b_2 s^2 + \dots} \tag{3.1}$$

A first condition on Eq. 3.1 is that the roots of $Q(s)$ must all lie in the left half plane. This condition follows from the passive nature of an *RLC* circuit, which prohibits growing natural oscillations. In the interest of simplicity, we shall assume that there are no roots of $Q(s)$ on the $j\omega$ axis (although, of course, ideal L's and C's could produce such a root), and that there are no roots of $Q(s)$ which are common to $P(s)$. If $Q(s)$ has all of its roots in the left half plane, then all b_i coefficients must have the same sign, which we shall assume is positive.

A second condition on Eq. 3.1 is that the a_i coefficients must have the same sign as the b_i coefficients. This follows from the assumptions that all R, L, and C components have positive values, the network contains no transformers, and there is a common terminal between input and output. A proof that all a_i are positive is omitted, but follows very easily from methods of topological circuit analysis.* The key fact is that all paths (in the RLC network) from I_1 to I_2 have a positive sense and traverse admittances which are positive for s positive real.

A third, and most important constraint on Eq. 3.1 is the condition that $a_i \leq b_i$ for all "i." In order to understand the origin of this constraint, note that $(I_1 - I_2)/I_1$ is *also* the current gain of a three-terminal transformerless network terminated in a passive load (short-circuit, in this case) as shown in Fig. 3.2. Therefore $[1 - (I_2/I_1)]$ must also have a numerator polynomial which has positive or zero coefficients; this is only true if $a_i \leq b_i$.

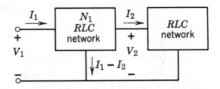

Fig. 3.2. Circuit for calculating gain limitations of N_1 in Fig. 3.1.

For simplicity of future discussion, we shall define I_2/I_1 for Fig. 3.2 as a "positive, passive gain" function or, for short, $PG(s)$. That is

if $0 \leq a_i \leq b_i$ for all i

and $Q(s) = 0$ only when $\text{Re}[s] < 0$

then $$\frac{P(s)}{Q(s)} = \frac{a_0 + a_1 s + \cdots}{b_0 + b_1 s + \cdots} \equiv PG(s) \qquad (3.2)$$

By considering a cascade of transformerless RLC networks, we can see that the product of two positive, passive gains is also a positive, passive gain.

In order to derive limits for the amplifier circuit of Fig. 3.1, we observe that the over-all current gain, $A_i(s) \equiv -I_4/I_1$, can be written as the product of passive circuit gains times the current gain of the transistor. By assuming that the *input admittance of the*

---

* See, for example, *Electronic Circuits, Signals, and Systems*, by S. J. Mason and H. J. Zimmermann, Wiley, New York, 1960, p. 59.

transistor is passive (i.e., can be approximated arbitrarily closely by a transformerless RLC circuit), we have the results

$$A_i(s) \equiv -\frac{I_4}{I_1}(s) = \frac{I_2}{I_1} \times \frac{-I_3}{I_2} \times \frac{I_4}{I_3} = \frac{-I_3}{I_2} \times PG(s)$$

By further assuming that the *output admittance of the transistor is passive* and given by y_{out}, we can write $-I_3/I_2$ as the product of the short-circuit current gain of the transistor, $h_f = y_f/y_i$, times the ratio $y_3/(y_3 + y_{out})$, where $y_3 = I_3/V_3$. Since this ratio is also a positive, passive gain, we reach the important conclusion

$$A_i(s) = \frac{y_f(s)}{y_i(s)} \times PG(s) \tag{3.3}$$

The application of Eq. 3.3 allows us to predict some important gain and speed limitations. In order to do so, however, we must express the over-all response $A_i(s)$ in a form which places clearly in evidence parameters identifiable as a "gain" and a "bandwidth."

Consider, first, the case where we wish the RLC networks and Y_L to be designed to yield $A_i(s)$ given by

$$A_i(s) = \frac{s}{c_0 + c_1 s + c_2 s^2} = \frac{1}{\dfrac{c_0}{s} + c_1 + c_2 s} \tag{3.4}$$

Many single-stage amplifiers have a response approximated by Eq. 3.4. Note that this type of response is characteristic of both broad-band amplifiers with constant gain over several decades of frequency, and narrow-band amplifiers with a bandwidth much less than the center frequency. Equation 3.4 is even characteristic of dc amplifiers if we let $c_0 = 0$.

We shall use the following definitions: ω_0 is the frequency at which the gain is maximum, $A_{i0} = A_i(j\omega_0)$ is the maximum (or mid-band) gain, and ω_h and ω_l are the upper and lower half-power frequencies. We then find

$$\omega_0{}^2 = \frac{c_0}{c_2} \tag{3.5a}$$

$$A_{i0} = \frac{1}{c_1} \tag{3.5b}$$

$$\omega_h - \omega_l = \frac{c_1}{c_2} \tag{3.5c}$$

In order to calculate constraints on A_{i0} and $(\omega_h - \omega_l)$, let us consider the case in which the transistor current gain, y_f/y_i, can be approximated by

$$\frac{y_f}{y_i} = \frac{\beta_0}{1 + s\beta_0/\omega_T} \tag{3.6}$$

The frequency range over which Eq. 3.6 is a good approximation is discussed in ECP, Chapter 3, but, typically, it is valid up to about $\omega_T/2$.

On combining Eqs. 3.3 through 3.6 we have

$$\frac{s[\beta_0^{-1} + \omega_T^{-1}s]}{c_0 + A_{i0}^{-1}s + [A_{i0}(\omega_h - \omega_l)]^{-1}s^2} = PG(s) \tag{3.7}$$

and, applying Eqs. 3.2 to Eq. 3.7, we find

$$\beta_0^{-1} \leq A_{i0}^{-1} \tag{3.8a}$$

$$\omega_T^{-1} \leq [A_{i0}(\omega_h - \omega_l)]^{-1} \tag{3.8b}$$

Equations 3.8 describe two intuitively reasonable constraints: (1) the mid-band amplifier current gain cannot exceed the transistor short-circuit current gain; and (2) the product of mid-band gain times half-power bandwidth of amplifier current gain cannot exceed ω_T. Note that there is no specific limitation on the center frequency, ω_0, except for the limitation on the validity of the analysis when ω_h gets high enough to invalidate the assumption of Eq. 3.6.

The analysis above does not guarantee that the limits of Eq. 3.8 can be realized, but only that no "better" response can be achieved within the scope of Eq. 3.4. However, in this case, the form of Eq. 3.4 and the upper limits on gain and bandwidth, as given in Eqs. 3.8, can very nearly be realized in practice. Two possible circuits are shown in Fig. 3.3, but there are also others, depending on the detailed input and output impedance characteristics of the transistor.

As a second example of the application of Eq. 3.3, we consider a form of current-gain frequency dependence which places in evidence a little more detail concerning speed of response than did Eq. 3.4. Specifically, we assume that $A_i(s)$ has the form

$$A_i(s) = \frac{A_{i0}}{1 + d_1s + d_2s^2 + \ldots} \tag{3.9}$$

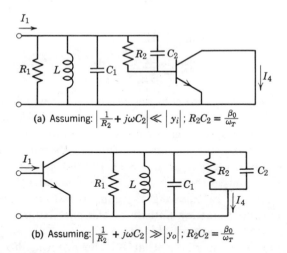

(a) Assuming: $\left| \frac{1}{R_2} + j\omega C_2 \right| \ll \left| y_i \right|$; $R_2 C_2 = \frac{\beta_0}{\omega_T}$

(b) Assuming: $\left| \frac{1}{R_2} + j\omega C_2 \right| \gg \left| y_o \right|$; $R_2 C_2 = \frac{\beta_0}{\omega_T}$

Fig. 3.3. Two possible circuits for achieving bounds of Eq. 3.8. Special cases: (1) $C_1 = 0$ for $A_{i0}(\omega_h - \omega_l) = \omega_T$; (2) $R_1 = \infty$ for $A_{i0} = \beta_0$; and (3) $L = \infty$ for $\omega_l = 0$.

and that the d_i coefficients are adjusted to give a monotonically increasing step response. It is then possible to equate amplifier *delay* to the coefficient d_1, as is discussed in MTC,* Chapter 8. That is, the total time required for the output to change from its initial value of 0, to 50% of its final value, is called the *delay*, and is given quite accurately by the coefficient d_1. The *rise time*, however, is the time that it takes for the output to go from 10% to 90% of its final value. This time may be much less than the delay, and there is no specific constraint between rise time and d_1 (actually, the 10% to 90% rise time with negligible overshoot is approximately given by $2.5 \sqrt{d_1^2 - 2d_2}$ for the reasons discussed in MTC, Chapter 8).

On combining Eqs. 3.3, 3.6, and 3.9, we have

$$\frac{A_{i0}(\beta_0^{-1} + s\omega_T)}{1 + d_1 s + d_2 s^2 + \cdots} = PG(s) \qquad (3.10)$$

---

* R. D. Thornton, C. L. Searle, D. O. Pederson, R. B. Adler, and E. J. Angelo, Jr., *Multistage Transistor Circuits*, Wiley, New York, 1965.

and, thus, the gain and speed limitations are

$$\beta_0^{-1} \leq A_{i0}^{-1} \tag{3.11a}$$

$$\omega_T^{-1} \leq \frac{d_1}{A_{i0}} \cong \frac{T_{\text{delay}}}{A_{i0}} \tag{3.11b}$$

In other words, when we consider responses for which there is a distinction between *delay* and *rise time* (or *bandwidth*), we find that ω_T does not impose a gain-bandwidth-product limitation, but rather a gain-per-delay limitation. For the special case treated previously (i.e., A_i given by Eq. 3.4), the half-power bandwidth was roughly equal to the reciprocal of the equivalent "delay" of the amplifier; but, by allowing the gain to fall off more rapidly with changes in frequency outside of the pass band, large gain-bandwidth products are possible for a given ω_T. A more detailed study would show, however, that for the rise time to be *much* less than the delay, the change in phase shift over the pass band must be very large, and hence the networks N_1 and N_2 must contain many L and C components. Thus we could not expect simple networks to accomplish a trade of delay for gain. It is of theoretical interest, however, to show that such a trade can be made.

As a first step in learning how a circuit might trade delay for gain, it is helpful to study the time-domain interpretation of Eqs. 3.11 as shown in Fig. 3.4. Notice that the bounds of Eqs. 3.11 can be represented as shown in Fig. 3.4 and are equivalent to

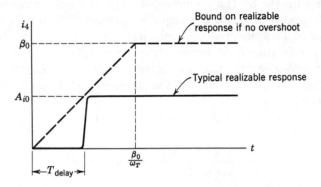

Fig. 3.4. Time-domain interpretation of bounds of Eq. 3.11, assuming that $i_1(t)$ is a unit step applied at $t = 0$, and $i_4(t)$ is monotonic.

the restrictions that the charge supplied to the transistor is always less than the charge supplied at the input, and the steady state current supplied to the transistor is always less than the current supplied at the input. (Note that these restrictions are valid only for the case of negligible oscillation in the step response.) One method of realizing the "typical response" shown in Fig. 3.4 is, therefore, to arrange for the input RLC circuit to store up the charge supplied by the source until suddenly at $t = T_{delay}$ the network delivers *all* of this stored charge to the transistor, thereby producing a very rapid increase of collector current. Actually, of course, there is a restriction on rise time, but it is not predicted by our analysis because of the assumed form of y_f/y_i (i.e., that Eq. 3.6 holds). If y_f/y_i for a transistor really varied as s^{-1} for large s, then there would, in fact, be no limit placed on rise time or bandwidth by the device itself!

One network which is capable of realizing a trade of delay for current gain is shown in Fig. 3.5, and a physical explanation of this circuit is as follows. The L and C elements form a lumped-circuit approximation to a delay line with characteristic impedance $R = \sqrt{L/C}$ and a delay of $T = (LC)^{-1/2}$ per section. When a step of current is applied at the input, this step travels

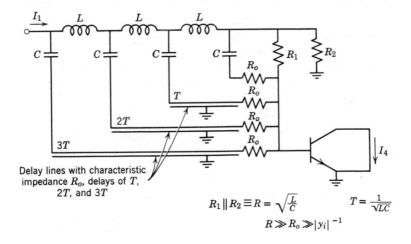

Fig. 3.5. One method of trading delay for current gain to achieve bounds of Eq. 3.11.

down the LC "transmission line," charging up the capacitors one by one. The capacitor current provides the input to another delay line which eventually delivers the charge to the transistor. By proper choice of the lengths of the secondary delay lines (which might also be approximated by LC circuits), all of the charging current for capacitors C can be made to arrive at the transistor at very nearly the same time. The net effect is that after a time equal to the total delay of the LC circuit, a near-impulse of current, or step of charge, is delivered to the transistor, and the rise time is limited only by the number of sections that one is willing to use in the LC delay line. After the "impulse" of current has been supplied to the transistor, the steady dc base current is delivered by R_1, so we achieve the desired output, a delayed step. Unfortunately, we must satisfy the impedance inequalities $R \gg R_o \gg r_{in}$, so the input voltage may be quite large. Although we can achieve large gain-bandwidth-products this way, it is usually much easier to use transistors in cascade in a multistage configuration when one requires large gains and bandwidths simultaneously.

Moreover, note that if all one needs is current gain, a simple transformer can be used to increase the gain without sacrificing bandwidth. It is obvious that an ideal transformer at the input can increase, arbitrarily, the current gain over any given frequency band, without introducing new delay. Thus, a large current-gain-bandwidth-product is available, independent of delay. Even a nonideal transformer may be used to circumvent the current-gain-speed limitations, as shown in Fig. 3.6. The transformer is used to supply high-frequency gain, while the transistor is the means for

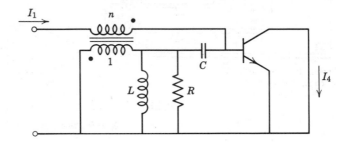

Fig. 3.6. One method of increasing current-gain-speed capabilities by means of a nonideal transformer.

supplying dc gain. Thus, wide bandwidth can be achieved without the need either to sacrifice current gain or to increase delay.

The deficiency of the foregoing analysis is now seen to be that we considered only current gain when, in fact, a useful transistor amplifier usually must also supply voltage gain and/or power gain. In short, ω_T, by itself, does not provide a complete measure of gain-speed capabilities.

3.1.2 *Voltage Gain*

The methods used to predict current-gain-speed limitations can also be used for determining voltage-gain limitations. In particular, if we replace y's by z's in Eq. 3.3, we have the limitation

$$A_v(s) \equiv \frac{-V_4}{V_1}(s) = \frac{-z_f(s)}{z_i(s)} \times PG(s) = \frac{y_f(s)}{y_o(s)} \times PG(s) \quad (3.12)$$

Thus the amplifier voltage gain is the product of the open-circuit transistor voltage gain, y_f/y_o, times the gain of a transformerless, three-terminal RLC circuit. Note that Eq. 3.12 requires the same conditions as Eq. 3.3: that the input and output impedances of the transistor be passive when it is connected to N_2 and N_1, respectively.

It is also usually possible to approximate y_f/y_o by a single-pole function over the frequency range of interest. Thus

$$\frac{y_f}{y_o} = \frac{\gamma_0}{1 + s\gamma_0/\omega_V} \quad (3.13)$$

where γ_0 and ω_V play roles analogous to β_0 and ω_T. This single-pole approximation can be justified on the basis of the physically-derived model of Fig. 3.7, or on the basis of typical measured values such as shown in Fig. 3.8. For the model of Fig. 3.7 we can calculate β_0, ω_T, γ_0, and ω_V by expressing y_f/y_i or y_f/y_o as a ratio $(a_0 + a_1 s + \cdots)/(b_0 + b_1 s + \cdots)$ and neglecting a_1, b_2, and all higher terms. The result is

$$\beta_0 \approx \frac{g_m}{g_\pi} \quad (3.14a)$$

$$\omega_T^{-1} \approx g_m^{-1}\left(C_\pi + C_\mu + C_{be} + C_{bc} + \frac{g_\pi}{g_x}[C_{bc} + C_{be}]\right) \quad (3.14b)$$

$$\gamma_0 \approx \frac{g_m g_x}{(g_x + g_\pi)(g_o + g_\mu)} \tag{3.14c}$$

$$\omega_V^{-1} \approx g_x^{-1} C_\mu + \gamma_0^{-1} \left[\frac{C_\mu + C_{be} + C_{ce}}{g_o + g_\mu} + \frac{C_\pi}{g_x + g_\pi} \right] \tag{3.14d}$$

where it is assumed that $g_m \gg g_o + g_\mu$ and $g_\pi \gg g_\mu$. For typical transistor parameters $g_x > g_\pi$, and the result can be approximated still further to

$$\beta_0 \approx \frac{g_m}{g_\pi} \qquad \omega_T^{-1} \approx \frac{C_\pi + C_\mu + C_{be} + C_{bc}}{g_m} \tag{3.15a,b}$$

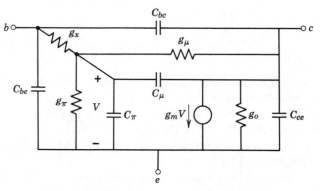

Fig. 3.7. Transistor model (from Fig. 3.12, ECP).

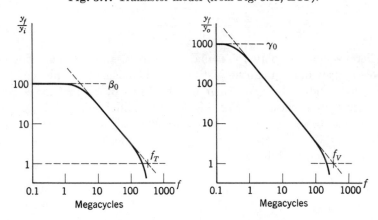

Fig. 3.8. Typical measured characteristics exhibiting single-pole approximation for y_f/y_i and y_f/y_o.

$$\gamma_0 \approx \frac{g_m}{g_o} \qquad \omega_V^{-1} \approx \frac{C_\mu}{g_x} + \frac{C_\mu + C_{bc} + C_{ce}}{g_m} \qquad (3.15c,d)$$

In so far as the single time constant approximation to y_f/y_o is valid, Eqs. 3.12 and 3.13 can be employed to derive voltage gain limitations analogous to those derived in Section 3.1.1 for current gain. For example, in an amplifier with a two-pole response, a mid-band voltage gain A_{v0}, and half power bandwidth $\omega_h - \omega_l$, we have the limitation $A_{v0}(\omega_h - \omega_l) \leq \omega_V$. Typically ω_V is greater than ω_T, so this limit is less stringent than the current gain limit; but for amplifiers with $A_{v0} \gg A_{i0}$, this ω_V limitation is quite important.

3.1.3 *Effect of Load*

The previous results can be extended to a more useful form by including the effect of a *specific* load impedance on the response. Figure 3.9 shows a three terminal passive RLC network coupling a transistor to a passive load admittance Y_c. The output of the transistor is represented by a current I_a in parallel with passive admittance Y_b.

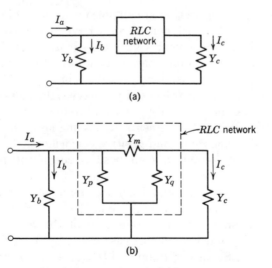

(a)

(b)

Fig. 3.9. Circuit for deriving Eq. 3.16. Y_b and Y_c are passive; Y_p, Y_m, and Y_q have left-half-plane poles.

We shall first derive the important result

$$\frac{I_c}{I_a} = \frac{Y_c}{Y_b + Y_c} \times PG(s) \qquad (3.16)$$

In words, Eq. 3.16 states that the current gain I_c/I_a can be written as the product of the gain that would exist with the transistor connected directly to the load, times a $PG(s)$ type function. The proof which follows may be omitted if the reader is willing to accept the validity of Eq. 3.16 and proceed directly to Eq. 3.18a.

Figure 3.9b shows the same circuit as Fig. 3.9a except that the RLC circuit has been replaced by three admittances Y_p, Y_m, and Y_q. This π-circuit representation is valid because an RLC circuit obeys reciprocity (if it did not, there would be four Y parameters required), but Y_p, Y_m, and Y_q need not be passive admittances (note that Y_p and Y_q are transfer admittances for *some* orientation of the RLC network). For convenience, we shall express the Y's as ratios of polynomials as follows

$$Y_b = \frac{P_b(s)}{Q(s)} \; ; \; Y_p = \frac{P_p(s)}{Q(s)} \; ; \; \cdots \; Y_c(s) = \frac{P_c(s)}{Q(s)} \qquad (3.17a)$$

The roots of polynomial $Q(s)$ are all pole frequencies of all Y's, and thus some of the $P(s)$ polynomials may have factors common with $Q(s)$. For all right-half-plane values of s, it is impossible for any RLC input or transfer admittance to be infinite (unless it is infinite for all frequencies). Thus, none of the Y's in Eqs. 3.17a can have right-half-plane poles. So $Q(s)$ can not have right-half-plane roots. We will exclude the possibility of natural frequencies for $s = j\omega$ on grounds that all L and C elements have some loss. Thus, $Q(s)$ will have left-half-plane roots, and positive coefficients.

The $P(s)$ polynomials are all positive-coefficient polynomials for the following reasons. First, $P_b(s)$ and $P_c(s)$ must have positive coefficients because $Y_b(s)$ and $Y_c(s)$ are assumed to be passive admittances (i.e. all poles *and* zeros are in the left half-plane). Next, note that the short-circuit current gain of the RLC circuit is a $PG(s)$ function, and it is in this case given by $Y_m/(Y_m + Y_p) = P_m/(P_m + P_p)$. So clearly $P_m(s)$ and $[P_m(s) + P_p(s)]$ are positive-coefficient polynomials. This is only possible if $P_m(s)$ and $P_p(s)$ are *both* positive coefficient polynomials. By a similar argument, $P_q(s)$ is also a positive coefficient polynomial.

We can now write the current gain I_c/I_a as follows

$$\frac{I_c}{I_a} = \frac{Y_c Y_m}{Y_m(Y_b + Y_p + Y_q + Y_c) + (Y_b + Y_p)(Y_q + Y_c)}$$

$$= \frac{Y_c}{Y_b + Y_c} \times$$

$$\frac{Y_m(Y_b + Y_c)}{Y_m(Y_b + Y_c) + [Y_m(Y_p + Y_q) + (Y_b + Y_p)(Y_q + Y_c)]}$$

$$= \frac{Y_c}{Y_b + Y_c} \times$$

$$\frac{P_m(P_b + P_c)}{P_m(P_b + P_c) + [P_m(P_p + P_q) + (P_b + P_p)(P_q + P_c)]}$$

$$= \frac{Y_c}{Y_b + Y_c} \times \frac{P_1(s)}{P_1(s) + P_2(s)} \tag{3.17b}$$

where

$$P_1(s) = P_m(P_b + P_c)$$

$$P_2(s) = P_m(P_p + P_q) + (P_b + P_p)(P_q + P_c)$$

Note that $P_1(s)$ and $P_2(s)$ are both positive coefficient polynomials in s, and thus $P_1/(P_1 + P_2)$ satisfies the conditions to be $PG(s)$, provided that $P_1(s) + P_2(s)$ has only left-half-plane roots. Since we know that I_c/I_a and $(Y_b + Y_c)/Y_c$ have only left-half-plane poles (e.g. Y_b and Y_c are passive), then clearly $P_1(s) + P_2(s)$ must have only left-half-plane roots. Thus, we know that Eq. 3.16 is true.

If we now draw the amplifier of Fig. 3.1 with transistor y parameters indicated specifically, as shown in Fig. 3.10, we have the relation

$$A_v(s) = \frac{-V_4}{V_1} = \frac{V_2}{V_1} \times y_f \times \frac{Y_L}{Y_L + y_o} \times PG_1(s) \times \frac{1}{Y_L}$$

$$= \frac{y_f}{y_o + Y_L} \times PG_2(s) = \frac{1}{y_o y_f^{-1} + Y_L y_f^{-1}} \times PG_2(s) \tag{3.18a}$$

and, similarly, for current gain replace y_i by z_i, y_f by $-z_f$, etc.

$$A_i(s) = \frac{-I_4}{I_1} = \frac{I_2}{I_1} \times z_f \times \frac{-Z_L}{Z_L + z_o} \times PG_3(s) \times \frac{1}{Z_L}$$

$$= \frac{-z_f}{z_o + Z_L} \times PG_4(s) = \frac{1}{y_i y_f^{-1} - Z_L z_f^{-1}} \times PG_4(s) \tag{3.18b}$$

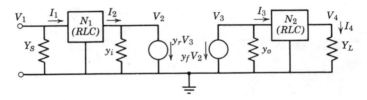

Fig. 3.10. Circuit of Fig. 3.1 indicating transistor parameters explicitly. (V_1, V_2, etc. measured with respect to ground.)

In short, the gain of the amplifier can be written as the product of the gain of the transistor when connected to the load *without* any coupling network, times the gain of a passive, three terminal, *RLC* network.

Consider, as a first example, the effect of a load capacitance C_L on the voltage gain-speed limitations. At frequencies less than about $\omega_b \equiv (g_x + g_\pi)/(C_\mu + C_\pi)$ (see MTC, Section 2.1), we can assume $y_f = g_m g_x/(g_x + g_\pi)$. Thus, using Eqs. 3.13 and 3.18a,

$$A_v(s) \approx \frac{1}{\gamma_0^{-1} + s(\omega_V^{-1} + [(g_x + g_\pi)/g_m g_x] sC_L)} \times PG(s)$$

In short, the *effective* value of ω_V^{-1} is given by

$$\omega_V^{-1}\,(\text{eff}) = \omega_V^{-1} + [(g_x + g_\pi)/g_m g_x]C_L$$

and the requirement of driving a load capacitance will definitely reduce the gain-speed capabilities of the transistor. In the case of a multistage amplifier, the input capacitance to the following stage is usually relatively large, and thereby seriously affects the value of $\omega_V(\text{eff})$.

As a second example, consider the effect of a load resistance R_L on the current gain-speed limitations. At moderate frequencies $z_f^{-1} \approx - s(C_\mu + C_{bc})$, (i.e., the value of z_f is determined by internal negative feedback) so we have, using Eqs. 3.6 and 3.18b,

$$A_i(s) \approx \frac{1}{\beta_0^{-1} + s[\omega_T^{-1} + R_L(C_\mu + C_{bc})]}$$

In short, the *effective* value of ω_T^{-1} is given by

$$\omega_T^{-1}\,(\text{eff}) = \omega_T^{-1} + R_L(C_\mu + C_{bc})$$

and the requirement of driving a load resistance has definitely reduced the gain-speed capabilities of the transistor. Thus, since the requirement of achieving midband voltage gain necessitates a nonzero R_L, the current gain-speed capabilities are reduced by the voltage gain requirements. This is closely related to the fact that the input capacitance to an amplifier includes C_μ and C_{bc} multiplied by the voltage gain of the stage.

3.1.4 *Unilateral Amplifier Gain-Speed Limitations*

The previous examples illustrate why in a multistage amplifier, where both current gain and voltage gain are required simultaneously, it is not possible to predict gain-speed capabilities by considering only ω_T and ω_V. Unfortunately, because of nonunilateral properties of the transistors, it is difficult to derive general multistage limitations. In this section we will treat the special case in which transistors are neutralized by suitable means, such as that shown in Fig. 3.11a, and identical stages are cascaded (i.e., the amplifier has "iterated" stages).

For the important special case where an amplifier consists of an iterated cascade of unilateral stages, it is possible to derive some relatively simple interrelations between gain and speed. We shall assume that the transistor is neutralized by means of a phase-reversing transformer and a passive feedback admittance, y_n, as shown in Fig. 3.11a. If the transistor is described by the model of Fig. 3.7, then y_n will have the form shown in Fig. 3.11b, although for a narrow-band amplifier y_n can usually be simplified to a single R and C. We shall designate the neutralized transistor y parameters as y_i', y_f', etc., and they are found to be

$$y_i' = y_i - ny_r \qquad\qquad y_r' = 0$$
$$y_f' = -n(y_f - y_r) \qquad\qquad y_o' = n^2 y_o - ny_r \qquad (3.19)$$
$$(\text{For } y_n = -ny_r)$$

Because the transistor is neutralized, the input admittance is y_i' and the output admittance is y_o'. Thus the per-stage gain is of the form

$$A_v(s) = A_i(s) \equiv A(s) = \frac{y_f'}{y_i' + y_o'} \times PG(s)$$

$$= \frac{-(y_f - y_r)}{n^{-1}y_i + ny_o - 2y_r} \times PG(s) \qquad (3.20)$$

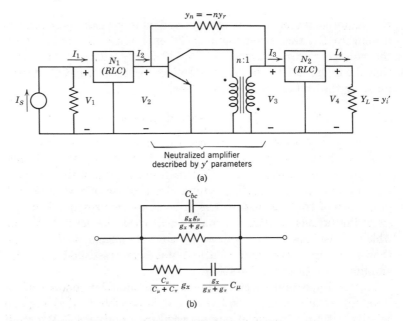

Fig. 3.11. Neutralized amplifier. (a) Circuit, (b) Neutralizing network.

We can usually neglect y_r in comparison with y_f, and y_f/y_r can usually be approximated by

$$\frac{y_f}{y_r} \cong \frac{-\omega_R}{s} ; \qquad \omega_R = \frac{g_m}{C_\mu + C_{bc}} \qquad (3.21)$$

Equation 3.20 then becomes

$$A(s) = \frac{-1}{(\beta_0^{-1} n^{-1} + \gamma_0^{-1} n) + s\tau_s} \times PG(s) \qquad (3.22)$$

where

$$\tau_s = \omega_T^{-1} n^{-1} + \omega_V^{-1} n + 2\omega_R^{-1}$$

For this iterated, unilateral amplifier example, τ_s plays the same role that ω_T^{-1} and ω_V^{-1} did in the preceding discussion of current gain and voltage gain limitations. Thus, τ_s is a reasonable measure of the speed capabilities of the neutralized transistor. For maximum speed we would adjust n for minimum τ_s with the results

$$\tau_s(\min) = 2[\sqrt{\omega_T^{-1}\omega_V^{-1}} + \omega_R^{-1}] \qquad (3.23)$$

for

$$n = \sqrt{\omega_V/\omega_T}$$

As a specific numerical example, for the transistor with characteristics given by Fig. 3.8, we have

$$\omega_T^{-1} = 1.08 \text{ ns}; \; \omega_V^{-1} = 0.85 \text{ ns}; \; \omega_R^{-1} = 0.11 \text{ ns}$$

$$\tau_s(\min) = 2.14 \text{ ns}; \; \frac{1}{2\pi\tau_s(\min)} = 74 \text{ mc/sec}$$

Thus, for a two-pole response of the form of Eq. 3.4, the product of per-stage bandwidth times per-stage gain cannot be greater than about 74 mc/sec. Note that even though the circuit utilizes a transformer in the interstage coupling network, the maximum gain-speed capabilities are only about half of what one would expect from considering ω_T or ω_V individually and *without* a transformer.

It should not be assumed that neutralization leads to the greatest possible speed; but, without neutralization, it is virtually impossible to identify *per-stage* gain or speed characteristics. Also, it is easy to show that in most practical amplifiers the internal feedback through the transistor (i.e., y_r) has an undesirable effect on bandwidth.

Note that the *effect* of neutralization can be accomplished by techniques other than those indicated in Fig. 3.11. For example, one can use a differential amplifier with cross-coupling admittances, as shown in Fig. 3.12a. Also, it is possible to use positive feedback around more than one stage, as shown in Fig. 3.12b. In fact, an amplifier which is designed to have negative feedback at low frequencies will, inevitably, have positive feedback at high frequencies where amplifier phase shift is important. Thus, even negative feedback may accomplish a partial cancellation of the effect of y_r. Phrased differently, internal feedback through y_r will cause splitting of the natural frequencies of a multistage amplifier (see, for example, MTC Chapter 1), and over-all negative feedback can decrease this splitting, much as does neutralization.

The circuits that we have considered previously have not allowed the use of series emitter impedances or shunt base-to-collector admittances. However, the addition of these elements will not change the conclusions significantly, *provided that the input and output admittances remain passive.* For example, a series emitter impedance decreases y_f and y_i in approximately the same ratio, and actually decreases the effective value of ω_T. However, in order

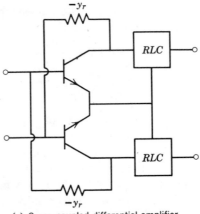

(a) Cross-coupled differential amplifier

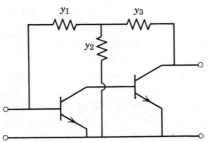

(b) Two-stage feedback neutralization; y_1, y_2, y_3 chosen
to approximately cancel effect of y_r in input stage

Fig. 3.12. Two methods of achieving the effect of neutralization.

to derive rigorous limitations for more general circuit configurations, including negative input and output admittances and non-unilateral stages, it is convenient to adopt a somewhat different approach.

3.2 MAXIMUM FREQUENCIES OF OSCILLATION

In the previous section, limitations were derived for a specific common-emitter configuration with restrictions on impedances. Although these limitations have significant practical importance, they do not necessarily imply unavoidable limitations. For example, suppose that we were willing to use any number of transistors and passive circuit components with no restriction on the circuit configuration or transistor parameters. This rather general circuit is represented by the schematic circuit diagram of Fig. 3.13 wherein the "coupling circuit," N, is composed of R, L, C, and transformer components. Our objective in this section is to derive some gain-speed limitations for this more general circuit.

Note that if the amplifier of Fig. 3.13 is to be capable of achieving power gain at a particular frequency, $s = j\omega$, then it should also be possible to feed the output power back to the input and produce oscillations. Clearly, the *passive* part of the circuit *cannot* produce any net output power for $s = j\omega$, so the important property of the *transistor* employed is *its* ability to deliver a net output power. We thus have the important constraint: *the power gain (ratio of output power to input power) of the whole amplifier must be less than unity, regardless of the load impedance, at any frequency $s = j\omega$ for which the transistor alone is incapable of delivering a net output power*. As an example, if the transistor is incapable of delivering output power for $\omega \geq \omega_{max}$, then the amplifier power gain must be less than or equal to unity for $\omega \geq \omega_{max}$. In this section we shall derive pertinent "maximum frequencies of oscillation," and then use these to derive some appropriate gain-speed limitations.

3.2.1 *Complex Power Derivation of* ω_{max}

For a one-port network (i.e., a network with only a single terminal-pair) excited by a sinusoid at frequency $s = j\omega$, the time-average power absorbed by the network is given by the real part of the complex power; that is

$$\overline{v(t) \times i(t)} = \tfrac{1}{2}\text{Re}[V^*I] = \text{Re}[P] \qquad (3.24)$$

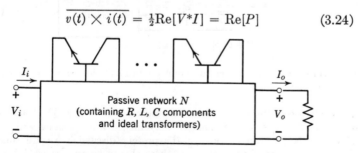

Fig. 3.13. Schematic representation of a general amplifier circuit.

where V^* is the complex conjugate of V, and V and I are complex magnitudes of the applied voltages and current. P is the complex power, and is defined here as†

$$P \equiv \tfrac{1}{2}V^*I = \text{complex power } absorbed\ by \text{ circuit} \qquad (3.25)$$

If V and I are related by $I = YV = (G + jB)V$, then

$$\text{Re}[P] = \tfrac{1}{2}\text{Re}[|V|^2(G + jB)] = \tfrac{1}{2}|V|^2 G \qquad (3.26)$$

Thus, if a one-port is to be capable of oscillating when connected to a passive network, then it must be capable of supplying a net power; so $G < 0$ is one important constraint. If $G < 0$, then it is possible to construct an oscillator by means of the circuit shown in Fig. 3.14; in this arrangement, the admittance of the passive circuit is made exactly equal to the negative of the admittance of the active one-port at the desired frequency of oscillation, ω_0. This condition insures that $s = +j\omega_0$ and $s = -j\omega_0$ will be natural frequencies of the circuit (although, of course, there may be others). For all known active one-ports, there is a *finite* frequency range $s = j\omega$ over which $G < 0$. As a specific example, if the model for the one-port is as shown in Fig. 3.15 with $r, g, C > 0$, then we have

$$G = \frac{-g(1 - rg) + \omega^2 r C^2}{(1 - rg)^2 + (\omega r C)^2} \qquad (3.27)$$

Therefore

$$G < 0 \qquad \text{only if} \quad \omega^2 < \frac{g(1 - rg)}{rC^2}, \qquad \text{and} \quad rg < 1$$

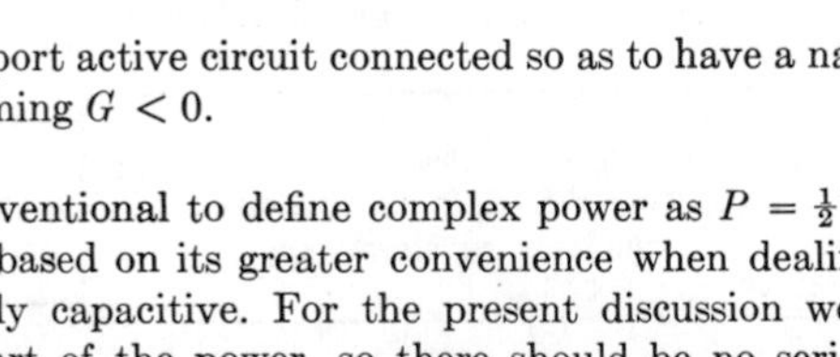

Fig. 3.14. One-port active circuit connected so as to have a natural frequency at $s = j\omega_0$, assuming $G < 0$.

† It is often conventional to define complex power as $P = \tfrac{1}{2}VI^*$. Our choice of $P = \tfrac{1}{2}V^*I$ is based on its greater convenience when dealing with devices which are largely capacitive. For the present discussion we are concerned with the real part of the power, so there should be no serious difficulty in interpreting the results from either point of view.

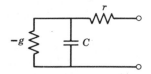

Fig. 3.15. Model for a hypothetical active one-port; $\omega^2_{max} = g(1 - rg)/rC^2$ if $rg < 1$ (r, g, and C assumed to be positive).

For a two-port active circuit, such as a transistor, the conditions for possible oscillation are more difficult to derive, although the principle is the same. We must still have $\mathrm{Re}[P] < 0$, but now P is the *sum* of the powers absorbed by the *two* ports. In other words, if V_1, V_2, I_1, and I_2 are the voltages and currents of the two ports, then for oscillation we must have

$$2\mathrm{Re}[P] = \mathrm{Re}[V_1^*I_1 + V_2^*I_2] < 0 \qquad (3.28)$$

Clearly we have some control over $\mathrm{Re}[P]$ because we can vary the magnitude ratio $|V_2/V_1|$ and the phase angle between V_2 and V_1. In order for oscillations to be *possible*, clearly there must be *some* choice of this ratio and angle which leads to $\mathrm{Re}[P] < 0$. Our problem is to find the conditions under which this is possible.

It is convenient to derive the conditions for possible oscillation in terms of h parameters. In particular, assume that the two-port is described by

$$\begin{aligned} V_1 &= h_i I_1 + h_r V_2 \\ I_2 &= h_f I_1 + h_o V_2 \end{aligned} \qquad (3.29)$$

P is then given by

$$\begin{aligned} 2P &= V_1^*I_1 + V_2^*I_2 \\ &= (h_i^*|I_1|^2 + h_r^*V_2^*I_1) + (h_f I_1 V_2^* + h_o|V_2|^2) \end{aligned} \qquad (3.30)$$

We can then express $\mathrm{Re}[P] \equiv P_R$ in the form:

$$\frac{2P_R}{|V_2 I_1|} = (h_{iR}a^{-1} + h_{oR}a) + \mathrm{Re}[(h_r^* + h_f)e^{-j\alpha}] \qquad (3.31)$$

where subscript R designates "real part of" (i.e., $P_R = \mathrm{Re}[P]$) and $V_2/I_1 \equiv ae^{j\alpha}$, $a > 0$.

The problem of interest is to determine whether there is any conceivable choice of a and α in Eq. 3.31 which will lead to a negative real-part for P. Note, first, that the second bracketed term in Eq. 3.31 has a fixed magnitude but a phase which can be adjusted at will by varying the angle α. The most negative that the real part of this term can possibly be is $|h_r^* + h_f|$. Thus, for $P_R < 0$, the first bracketed term in Eq. 3.31 cannot be more positive than $|h_r^* + h_f|$. Of course, if either h_{iR} or h_{oR} is negative, then we can always make the first term negative simply by making a either very small or very large. However, the problem of greatest interest is to calculate the conditions of oscillation when h_{iR} and h_{oR} are both positive. In this case we minimize the magnitude of the first term in Eq. 3.31 by choosing $a = \left|\sqrt{h_{iR}/h_{oR}}\right|$. In short

$$\left.\frac{2P_R}{|V_2 I_1|}\right|_{\text{most neg.}} = 2\left|\sqrt{h_{iR}h_{oR}}\right| - |h_r^* + h_f| \tag{3.32}$$

In summary, there are three conditions under any *one* of which P_R can be negative for some choice of a and α.

$$\begin{align}
&(1) \quad h_{iR} < 0 \\
&(2) \quad h_{oR} < 0 \tag{3.33} \\
&(3) \quad |h_f + h_r^*|^2 > 4|h_{iR}h_{oR}|
\end{align}$$

The conditions of Eq. 3.33 are the important results of the analysis, and will now be interpreted. Condition *1* is the obvious condition that if the input impedance with output shorted has a negative real part, then an oscillator can be built along the lines of Fig. 3.14. Likewise, for condition *2*, if $h_{oR} < 0$, then a passive circuit connected across port 2 can produce oscillations (when port 1 is open-circuited, in this case).

Condition *3* in Eq. 3.33 is peculiar to a two-port, and needs additional interpretation. First, it is helpful to write this condition in a slightly different form using the general notation $h = h_R + jh_I$. Note that, if

$$|h_f + h_r^*|^2 > 4h_{iR}h_{oR} \qquad \text{for} \quad h_{iR}h_{oR} \geq 0 \tag{3.34}$$

then, by adding $4h_{fI}h_{RI}$ to each side of Eq. 3.34, we have

$$|h_f + h_r|^2 > 4[h_{iR}h_{oR} + h_{fI}h_{rI}]$$

or

$$U > 1 \qquad \text{where} \quad U = \frac{|h_f + h_r|^2}{4[h_{iR}h_{oR} + h_{fI}h_{rI}]} \tag{3.35}$$

Thus, it is possible for P_R to be less than zero when h_{iR} and h_{oR} are nonnegative if, and only if, $U > 1$, where U is defined in Eq. 3.35. The parameter U can also be written in terms of y-parameters by means of the identities

$$h_f + h_r = \frac{y_f - y_r}{y_i}$$

$$h_{iR}h_{oR} + h_{fI}h_{rI} = |y_i|^{-2}[y_{iR}y_{oR} - y_{fR}y_{rR}]$$

giving

$$U = \frac{|y_f - y_r|^2}{4[y_{iR}y_{oR} - y_{fR}y_{rR}]} \tag{3.36}$$

From Eq. 3.36 we observe that if the two-port obeys reciprocity, then $y_f = y_r$ and $U = 0$. Hence, U is nonzero only for *nonreciprocal* two-ports. For example, if a two-port obeys reciprocity, then the only possible hope for constructing an oscillator is to find a negative real part to the admittance (and impedance) at one of the terminal pairs with the other terminal pair open or shorted (e.g., one must have either $h_{iR} < 0$ or $h_{oR} < 0$). However, if at some frequency ω_0, $U > 1$, we have seen that there is a possibility of extracting net power from the two-port at that frequency, even though h_i and h_o (and y_i and y_o) have positive real parts. Thus, at such a frequency it must be possible to make an amplifier with power gain, which delivers more power output than it receives as power input. Correspondingly, it must also be possible for such an amplifier to supply from its output (at least) its own power input. Accordingly, if $U \geq 1$ at $s = \pm j\omega_0$, an oscillator can be constructed by feeding the output back to the input with appropriate phase shift, and providing suitable additional network elements to adjust the impedances for maximum power transfer from the output to the input. Such an arrangement is shown in Fig. 3.16, and an alternative oscillator circuit appears in Fig. 3.17. There, the reactances L_1, L_2, and C provide both the phase-shifted feedback and the adjustment of impedances for maximum power transfer.

In general, for a given active-circuit model, such as that for a transistor under specified bias conditions, the parameter U is a function of frequency. Often $U(\omega) > 1$ at some frequencies and $U(\omega) < 1$ at others. In many cases (for example, a transistor),

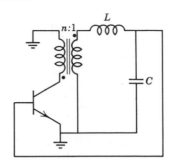

Fig. 3.16. Transformer-feedback oscillator for producing oscillations at $s = j\omega_{max}$.

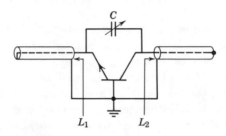

Fig. 3.17. Transformerless version of Fig. 3.16 using shorted transmission lines as high frequency inductors (or capacitors).

$U(\omega) > 1$ at low frequencies, and drops off steadily at high frequencies. In such cases, there is an ω_{max} such that

$$U(\omega_{max}) = 1 \qquad (3.37a)$$

$$U(\omega) > 1 \text{ for } \omega < \omega_{max} \qquad (3.37b)$$

$$U(\omega) < 1 \text{ for } \omega > \omega_{max} \qquad (3.37c)$$

Thus clearly, in this case, ω_{max} is the highest frequency at which $U \geq 1$, and it is therefore the maximum frequency ω at which the device under the given bias conditions can be made to oscillate steadily, no matter what combinations of R's, L's, C's, and ideal transformers may be employed with it.

In fact, for a given two-port it can be shown that the value of the parameter U is not altered at all by any arrangements of L's,

C's, and ideal transformers (*i.e. any lossless, reciprocal elements*) within which the device may be interconnected to make a new two-port.†

An example of this fact can be used to interpret U as follows. Any two-port can be made unilateral at a given frequency ω by use of lossless, reciprocal, network elements. Figure 3.18 shows

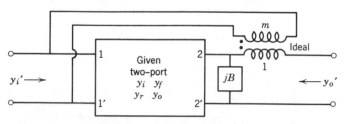

Fig. 3.18. Method of using lossless reciprocal elements to make a two-port unilateral ($y_r' = 0$). Notice that $\mathrm{Re}[y_o'] = \mathrm{Re}[y_o]$.

such an arrangement for canceling y_r of the given network, and creating a new two-port with $y_r' = 0$. The susceptance jB is used to adjust the phase angle of the output current response to an applied voltage at the output terminals, with the input shorted. The magnitude and sign of the turns ratio m is used to adjust the magnitude and quadrant of the current fed back, so that it will just oppose that produced by y_r of the given two-port. Observe that $y_{oR}' = y_{oR}$ in this arrangement. Then, for the special case $y_r' = 0$, note that U is given by

$$U = \frac{|y_f'|^2}{4y_{iR}'y_{oR}'} \qquad (3.38)$$

We can interpret U in Eq. 3.38 as the "power gain" of the *unilateral* amplifier with a conjugate-matched load admittance, as shown in Fig. 3.19. The power gain of interest to us here is defined as the small signal output power per unit small signal input power

$$G_p = \frac{\mathrm{Re}[V_2^* I_2]}{\mathrm{Re}[V_1^* I_1]} = \left|\frac{V_2}{V_1}\right|^2 \frac{G_L}{y_{iR}} = \left|\frac{y_f'}{y_o' + Y_L}\right|^2 \frac{G_L}{y_{iR}} \qquad (3.39)$$

and, for a conjugate-matched load,

† S. J. Mason, "Power Gain in Feedback Amplifiers," *Trans. IRE*, PGCT, CT-1, No. 2, p. 20 (1954).

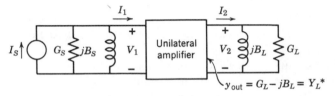

Fig. 3.19. Amplifier with conjugate-matched load impedances.

$$G_p = G_p(\max) = \frac{|y_f'|^2}{4y_{iR}'y_{oR}'}$$

for

$$Y_L = y_o'^* \tag{3.40}$$

On comparing Eq. 3.40 with Eq. 3.38, we see that for the special case $y_r' = 0$, U is exactly equal to the maximum available power gain. Thus, we can understand why U is called the "unilateral gain" of the device; but it must be emphasized that it is the maximum power gain of the device when it has been made unilateral by using *only lossless reciprocal* elements. If the original network were rendered unilateral by using, instead, elements with losses, or those which do not obey reciprocity, then the gain of the resulting *unilateral* amplifier might be either *greater or less* than U!

Also included among the above-mentioned interconnections of a given device with lossless, reciprocal network elements (often described as "lossless, reciprocal imbeddings") is the change of input and output terminal-pair selection to make a new two-port from a three-terminal network (these selections can be accomplished by using ideal transformers). For example, U is exactly the same for the common-base, common-emitter, and common-collector connections of a given transistor under given bias conditions.

Similarly, the maximum frequency of oscillation $\omega_{\max}$ for a transistor is characteristic of the transistor and its bias, and the circuit of Fig. 3.17 is particularly convenient for measuring $\omega_{\max}$ by adjusting L_1, L_2, and C to produce the highest frequency of oscillation (in some cases, L and C elements may have to be interchanged). Note that to achieve the maximum frequency of oscillation it normally takes at least three passive components to provide the required conjugate impedance matching, and the correct phase of the feedback signal. This result coincides with the fact that an arbitrary, lossless, reciprocal two port can, at a single frequency $s = j\omega$, be described by three parameters (e.g., y_{iI}, y_{oI}, and $y_{rI} = y_{fI}$).

The maximum frequency-of-oscillation characteristic of the transistor under given bias conditions can be computed readily for the model of Fig. 3.7. First, note that the extrinsic capacitances C_{be}, C_{ce}, and C_{bc} can all be "tuned out" by resonating them with appropriate values of inductance. In other words, these capacitances will have no effect on the unilateral power gain, $U(\omega)$, because of the invariance of U to lossless, reciprocal imbedding. Also, at high enough frequencies, g_π, g_o, and g_μ will have very little effect on available power gain and hence may, very probably, be neglected in calculating $\omega_{\max}$ (we should check this assumption after finding $\omega_{\max}$). Thus, the problem of interest is to calculate the maximum frequency of oscillation for the model of Fig. 3.20. The calculation is simplest algebraically when done in terms of common-emitter h-parameters, which are as follows

$$h_i = r_x + \frac{1}{s(C_\pi + C_\mu)}; \qquad h_r = \frac{C_\mu}{C_\mu + C_\pi}$$

$$h_f = \frac{g_m}{s(C_\pi + C_\mu)} - \frac{C_\mu}{C_\mu + C_\pi}; \quad h_o = \frac{C_\mu}{C_\mu + C_\pi}(g_m + sC_\pi) \tag{3.41}$$

We thus find that, for $s = j\omega$, U is given by

$$U = \frac{|h_f + h_r|^2}{4[h_{iR}h_{oR} + h_{fI}h_{rI}]} = \frac{|g_m/(C_\pi + C_\mu)\omega|^2}{4r_x g_m C_\mu/(C_\pi + C_\mu)} = \left(\frac{\omega_{\max}}{\omega}\right)^2 \tag{3.42}$$

where

$$\omega_{\max}^2 = \frac{g_m}{4r_x C_\mu(C_\pi + C_\mu)} \tag{3.43}$$

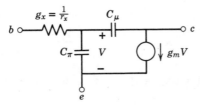

Fig. 3.20. Transistor model for computing $\omega_{\max}$.

For $\omega^2 < \omega_{max}^2$, we have $U > 1$, so oscillations are possible; but observe that the unlimited increase of U at frequencies much below ω_{max} predicted by Eq. 3.42 is incorrect, because of the high-frequency assumptions made directly in the model of Fig. 3.20. Actually, U levels off at low frequencies to a large value easily calculated from the low-frequency form of Fig. 3.7. On the other hand, Eqs. 3.41 and 3.42 show, correctly, that for $\omega^2 > \omega_{max}^2$, $U < 1$ and h_{oR}, $h_{iR} > 0$. So there is no possibility for useful power gain, and sustained oscillations are not possible. Thus, ω_{max} represents an important limitation which cannot be avoided by the cleverest of circuit design.

On comparing Eq. 3.43 with Eqs. 3.14 we see that, in general,

$$\omega_{max}^2 > \tfrac{1}{4}\,\omega_V \omega_T \tag{3.44a}$$

but, for the common situation,

$$g_m \gg g_x \gg g_\pi \quad \text{and} \quad C_\pi + C_\mu \gg C_{be} + C_{bc}$$

we have

$$\omega_{max}^2 \cong \tfrac{1}{4}\omega_V \omega_T \tag{3.44b}$$

In short, except at low-bias currents where g_m and C_π are small, the maximum frequency of oscillation, ω_{max}, is approximately one half of the geometric mean of ω_T and ω_V, and thus this mean has significance as an *ultimate* limit on *bandwidth*. Under no conditions can any transistor amplifier have an input-to-output power gain greater than unity for $\omega \geq \omega_{max}$. This is a true limitation on ω_h, not just a gain-bandwidth product or a gain-per-delay limitation.

In order to understand further the significance of the ω_{max} limit, it is helpful to reexamine some common-emitter examples similar to those treated earlier. Consider, first, the case of an "iterated amplifier," in which, by definition the input impedance of each stage is the same as its load impedance (both *assumed* to be *passive*). In this case, A_v and A_i are equal, and we assume that they have the same two pole response as in Eq. 3.4. That is

$$A_v = A_i = A = \frac{s}{c_0 + c_1 s + c_2 s^2} \tag{3.45}$$

where: $\qquad A\,(\text{max}) = A_0 = \dfrac{1}{c_1} \quad \text{at} \quad \omega^2 = \omega_0^2 = \dfrac{c_0}{c_2}$

$$A_0(\omega_h - \omega_l) = \frac{1}{c_2}$$

Because of the iterated nature assumed for this amplifier, the power gain *per stage* (for $s = j\omega$) is given by

$$G_P = |A|^2 = \frac{\omega^2}{(c_0 - c_2\omega^2)^2 + (c_1\omega)^2} \tag{3.46}$$

An important speed limitation is then found by requiring that the power gain of this whole stage not exceed the limitation of the transistor—that is, $G_P \leq 1$ for $\omega^2 \geq \omega_{max}^2$. Thus

$$\omega_{max}^2 \leq (c_1\omega_{max})^2 + (c_0 - c_2\omega_{max}^2)^2 \tag{3.47}$$

or, on using the relations in Eq. 3.45, we find

$$A_0^2 - 1 \leq \left(\frac{\omega_{max}}{\omega_h - \omega_l}\right)^2\left(1 - \left[\frac{\omega_0}{\omega_{max}}\right]^2\right) \tag{3.48}$$

For the common case where $A_0^2 \gg 1$ and $\omega_0^2 \ll \omega_{max}^2$ Eq. 3.48 reduces to the familiar form

$$A_0(\omega_h - \omega_l) < \omega_{max} \tag{3.49}$$

In other words, for the special case of a single pole-pair response given by Eq. 3.45, the product of mid-band voltage or current gain times the half-power bandwidth cannot exceed ω_{max}.

Note that the neutralized amplifier discussed in Sec. 3.1.3 led to a gain-bandwidth product limitation of

$$|A_0|(\omega_h - \omega_l) \leq \tfrac{1}{2}[\sqrt{\omega_T^{-1}\omega_V^{-1}} + \omega_R^{-1}]^{-1}$$

but, for a typical case where $\omega_T^{-1}\omega_V^{-1} \gg \omega_R^{-2}$, and $\omega_{max}^2 \approx \omega_T\omega_V/4$ (Eq. 3.44b), we have

$$A_0(\omega_h - \omega_l) < \tfrac{1}{2}\left|\sqrt{\omega_T\omega_V}\right| \approx \omega_{max} \tag{3.50}$$

Equation 3.50 demonstrates that for typical parameter values the common-emitter amplifier of Fig. 3.11 is almost capable of realizing the "best possible" performance. However, if ω_h becomes comparable to ω_{max}, Eq. 3.48 implies more rigid restrictions than were derived previously.

As a second example of the speed limitations implied by ω_{max}, consider the case of a wide-band amplifier with negligible overshoot. Typically, such an amplifier has many nearly equal poles and the gain can be approximated by the Gaussian form $|A| \approx |A_0|e^{-a\omega^2}$. It is thus of interest to know what gain-bandwidth limitations there are for this type of response. Clearly, the larger the gain, the smaller the bandwidth must be in order to insure that the power gain is less than unity for $\omega > \omega_{max}$. For simplicity, assume that the amplifier has resistive input and output impedances and, for a matched load, has a current gain A_i and a voltage gain A_v given by

$$
\begin{aligned}
|A_v| &= |A_{v0}|e^{-a\omega^2} \\
|A_i| &= |A_{i0}|e^{-a\omega^2}
\end{aligned}
\tag{3.51}
$$

The power gain, assuming resistive input and matched resistive output impedances, is given by

$$G_P = |A_v A_i| \tag{3.52}$$

We thus have the speed limitation

$$|A_{v0}A_{i0}|e^{-2a\omega^2} \leq 1 \qquad \text{for} \quad \omega^2 \geq \omega_{max}^2 \tag{3.53}$$

If we recognize that $2a$ can be identified as

$$2a = \omega_h^{-2} \ln 2 \tag{3.54}$$

We find that Eq. 3.53 reduces to

$$\omega_h^2 \ln |A_{v0}A_{i0}| \leq \omega_{max}^2 \ln 2 \tag{3.55}$$

Equation 3.55 describes a gain-bandwidth limitation which has an interesting physical interpretation. Note that for a unilateral, iterated-stage amplifier of this general type, if A_{01} is the low-frequency voltage and current gain per stage, then for n stages the gain is A_{01}^n. Also, if ω_{h1} is the bandwidth for one stage, then the bandwidth for n stages is approximately $\omega_{h1}/\sqrt{n}$, for reasons discussed in MTC, Chapter 8. We thus find

$$\omega_h^2 \ln |A_{v0}A_{i0}| = \frac{\omega_{h1}^2}{n} \ln A_{01}^{2n} = \omega_{h1}^2 \ln A_{01}^2 \tag{3.56}$$

Thus, the product of log-power-gain times bandwidth squared is not changed by cascading. If we wish the over-all amplifier to have the maximum possible product of log-power-gain times bandwidth squared, then we only need maximize this quantity for individual stages.

As a specific example, assume identical, unilateral stages are cascaded in order to produce overall gains $A_{v0} = A_{i0} = A_0$, with Gaussian-like frequency response. Typically, the individual stages will have a single pole response ($\omega_l = 0$) with a gain-band-width-product limitation of the form (see Eq. 3.22 and following):

$$A_{01}\omega_{h1} = \tau_{\min}^{-1} \tag{3.57}$$

For this case, maximum ω_h requires $A_{01}^2 = e$; that is,

$$\omega_{h1}^2 \ln A_{01}^2 \bigg|_{\max} = \tau_{\min}^{-2} \frac{\ln A_{01}^2}{A_{01}^2}\bigg|_{\max} = \tau_{\min}^{-2} e^{-1} \text{ (for } A_{01}^2 = e) \tag{3.58}$$

If $\tau_{\min}^{-2}(e \ln 2)^{-1}$ is not much smaller than $\omega_{\max}^2$, then ω_h is near the maximum given by Eq. 3.55 (see Problem P3.9).

If the transistor operating point is chosen for maximum speed, then typically $\tau_{\min}^{-1} \approx \omega_{\max}$ (Eq. 3.50), and cascaded stages produce near-maximum values of $\omega_{h1}^2 \ln A_0^2$. However, for some transistors, or at low bias currents, $\tau_{\min}^{-1}$ is much smaller than $\omega_{\max}$. Then non-cascade amplifiers, such as the "distributed amplifier," may be attractive. A typical distributed amplifier is shown in Fig. 3.21; this is a circuit built in the form of a delay line. It allows one to trade delay for gain when both current and voltage gain are required. Ideally the input signal propagates along the base circuit delay line (i.e., L_1, C_1) causing the transistor collector currents to change in time sequence. These currents are then added by means of a collector delay line (i.e., L_2, C_2) which restores the time coherence of the signal. This type of circuit does not, of course, circumvent the $\omega_{\max}$ limitation (Eq. 3.55).

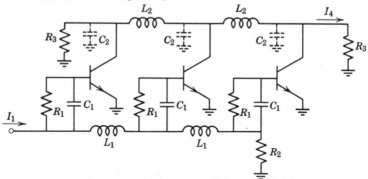

Fig. 3.21. Simplified three-stage distributed amplifier.

In summary, note that Eq. 3.55 describes an important and, many times, an almost achievable upper bound on simultaneous achievement of gain and bandwidth. However, for $\omega_h \ll \omega_{max}$, the limit of Eq. 3.55 is almost meaningless; for example, if $\omega_h = 0.1\omega_{max}$, then the theoretical gain "limit" is more than 600 db! Note that if we do not limit ourselves to a Gaussian-like response, then for high-gain amplifiers the only real bandwidth limitation is $\omega_h < \omega_{max}$; but to achieve ω_h values near to ω_{max} would require exceedingly fast fall off of gain with frequency for $\omega > \omega_h$. This, in turn, implies a relatively complex configuration of transistors, L's, and C's, and a step response which has considerable overshoot.

3.2.2 *Speed Limitations Implied by* σ_{max}

In many instances of practical importance, a transistor model which is both useful and accurate predicts either infinite, or unreasonably large values of ω_{max}. For example, Fig. 3.22 shows a transistor model which is quite accurate for transistors operated at frequencies below about $\omega_b = (g_x + g_\pi)/(C_\pi + C_\mu)$, or for somewhat higher frequencies when a series emitter resistor is used. This model is discussed in more detail in MTC, Chapter 2. It predicts $\omega_{max} = \infty$ because all capacitors can be "tuned out" with inductors, leaving only a frequency-independent circuit model with, presumably, a power gain greater than unity. This model does have finite values of ω_T and ω_V, however, so it is of interest to determine whether the common-emitter limitations implied by ω_T and ω_V are avoidable by use of some other circuit configuration, or whether there is some other basic limitation. Note that even though there

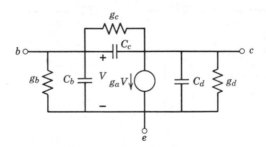

Fig. 3.22. Useful transistor model for low bias currents and/or low-to-moderate frequencies.

may be no *bandwidth* limitation, there may be an important *delay* (or phase shift) limitation. For example, if this transistor is used in a feedback amplifier, phase shift leads to stability problems when the loop gain is large; we would like to know whether this phase shift is unavoidable or, like the undesirable "feedback" attributes of $C\mu$, whether it might be nullified by appropriate circuit design.

One approach to calculating speed limitations for the transistor of Fig. 3.22 is to recognize that the "maximum frequency of oscillation" approach need not be restricted to $s = j\omega$ but, for example, can be applied to the case $s = \sigma$. In short, we can calculate a $\sigma_{\max}$ as well as an $\omega_{\max}$ and we have the similar restriction that the power gain must be less than unity for $\sigma > \sigma_{\max}$.

Note that for $s = \sigma > 0$ all positive-value inductors and capacitors have positive, real admittances; so the model of Fig. 3.22 becomes purely resistive. If we calculate the total power absorbed, and determine the conditions under which a *net* output power is possible, the previously derived conditions of Eqs. 3.33 are still applicable. In particular, the important consideration is that for h_{iR} and h_{oR} positive, net output is possible if and only if $U > 1$, where U is the same as given by Eqs. 3.35 and 3.36. Of course, for $s = \sigma$, $y_R = y$, and $h_R = h$, so the real-part designation is unnecessary, but correct. For transistor models it is usually true that with $s = \sigma > 0$ we find h_{iR}, $h_{oR} > 0$ and $U > 1$ for, and only for, σ less than a critical value, which we will call $\sigma_{\max}$. That is, by analogy with Eqs. 3.37,

$$U(\sigma_{\max}) = 1 \tag{3.59a}$$

$$U(\sigma) > 1 \text{ for } \sigma < \sigma_{\max} \tag{3.59b}$$

$$U(\sigma) < 1 \text{ for } \sigma > \sigma_{\max} \tag{3.59c}$$

As an example of the calculation of $\sigma_{\max}$, consider the transistor model of Fig. 3.22 with the additional assumption that for $s = \sigma_{\max}$ we can make the approximations:

$$s(C_b + C_e) \gg g_b + g_c; \quad sC_e \gg g_c; \quad \text{and} \quad s(C_e + C_d) \gg g_c + g_d$$

We then have for the y parameters near $s = \sigma_{\max}$:

$$y_i \cong s(C_b + C_e) \qquad y_r \cong -sC_e$$

$$y_f \cong g_a - sC_e \qquad y_o \cong s(C_e + C_d)$$

and the "unilateral gain," U is

$$U \cong \frac{|g_a|^2}{s^2(C_b C_e + C_b C_d + C_e C_d) + s g_a C_e} \text{ for } s = \sigma \text{ near } \sigma_{\max} \quad (3.60)$$

According to Eq. 3.59a we then have

$$1 \cong \frac{|g_a|^2}{\sigma_{\max}^2 (C_b C_e + C_b C_d + C_e C_d) + \sigma_{\max} g_a C_e}$$

or

$$\sigma_{\max} \cong \frac{|g_a|}{2[C_e + |\sqrt{(C_b + C_e)(C_d + C_e)}|]} \quad (3.61)$$

Equation 3.61 can be put in a somewhat more convenient form by rewriting it in terms of previously defined parameters ω_T, ω_V, and ω_R

$$\omega_T \cong \frac{g_a}{C_b + C_e} \; ; \; \omega_V \cong \frac{g_a}{C_d + C_e} \; ; \text{ and } \omega_R \cong \frac{g_a}{C_e}$$

Thus

$$\sigma_{\max}^{-1} \cong 2[\sqrt{\omega_T^{-1} \omega_V^{-1}} + \omega_R^{-1}] \quad (3.62)$$

On comparing Eq. 3.62 with Eq. 3.23 we see that $\sigma_{\max}^{-1} \cong \tau_s(\min)$ where τ_s was the speed measure used for the neutralized transformer-coupled common-emitter amplifier of Fig. 3.11. This near equality between $\sigma_{\max}^{-1}$ and $\tau_s(\min)$ strongly suggests that $\tau_s(\min)$ represents some kind of fairly basic limitation.

One interpretation of the $\sigma_{\max}$ limitation can be seen by considering the same example used to study the $\omega_{\max}$ limitation. A derivation analogous to Eqs. 3.45 to 3.48 leads to (Problem P3.6)

$$(A_0 - 1)(\omega_h - \omega_l) \le \sigma_{\max} \left(1 + \frac{\omega_0^2}{\omega_{\max}^2}\right) \quad (3.63a)$$

For the common case where $A_0^2 \gg 1$ and $\omega_0^2 \ll \omega_{\max}^2$, Eq. 3.63a reduces to

$$A_0(\omega_h - \omega_l) < \sigma_{\max} \quad (3.63b)$$

Since $\sigma_{\max}$ is usually less than $\omega_{\max}$, Eq. 3.63b implies a more severe restriction than Eq. 3.49.

Actually, of course, $\sigma_{\max}$ does not imply any absolute bandwidth limitation, since we can, presumably, exchange delay for gain without reducing bandwidth. For example, suppose that we want to achieve very large gain and bandwidth, with the minimum possible delay. If we assume infinite bandwidth with A of the form

$$A = A_v = A_i = A_0 e^{-T_{\text{delay}}s}$$

then we must have

$$|A|^2 \leq 1 \qquad \text{for} \quad s \geq \sigma_{\max}$$

or

$$A_0{}^2 e^{-2T_{\text{delay}}\sigma_{\max}} \leq 1$$

and thus

$$\frac{\ln A_0}{T_{\text{delay}}} \leq \sigma_{\max} \qquad (3.64)$$

Equation 3.64 has a simple interpretation. If we cascade several stages of gain, the decibels of power gain (i.e. $4.6 \ln A_0$) are proportional to the number of stages, but the delay is also proportional to the number of stages. So, $\ln A_0/T_{\text{delay}}$ is not changed by cascading, and must be less than $\sigma_{\max}$. Thus the method of achieving the bound of Eq. 3.64 is to maximize the ratio $\ln A_0/T_{\text{delay}}$ for each stage, and then cascade enough stages to achieve the desired overall gain. For example, by means of the circuit of Fig. 3.11 we can achieve, approximately, $A_0/T_{\text{delay}} = \sigma_{\max}$. Thus, for one stage,

$$\frac{\ln A_0}{T_{\text{delay}}} = \frac{\ln A_0}{A_0}\sigma_{\max}$$

This expression is maximum when $A_0 = e$, and accordingly

$$\frac{\ln A_0}{T_{\text{delay}}} (\max) = \frac{1}{e}\sigma_{\max}$$

Thus we can come within a factor e of realizing the minimum possible delay by cascading a number of common emitter stages, each with a gain of about $A_0 = e$.

In this chapter we have, in several instances, derived expressions for $\omega_{\max}$ and $\sigma_{\max}$ in terms of simplified transistor models which were *not* valid at frequencies in the vicinity of $s = j\omega_{\max}$ and $s = \sigma_{\max}$. Thus, for example, the expression for $\omega_{\max}$ in Eq. 3.43 is *not* the maximum frequency at which oscillations could be observed in the laboratory. However, this difference between model and transistor need not limit the usefulness of the derived value of $\omega_{\max}$. Remember for example, that ω_T and ω_V are *not* the frequencies at which the current and voltage gain are unity, but only the frequencies at which the gains *would* be unity if the lower frequency model were extrapolated beyond its range of validity. As long as the model is valid for the frequencies of interest in the amplifier analysis, we can reasonably use the model to calculate gain-speed limitations, and parameters such as ω_T, ω_V, $\omega_{\max}$, and $\sigma_{\max}$, are convenient terms in which to express these limitations.

In summary, we see that $\sigma_{\max}$ does not imply any restriction on bandwidth, but it does imply a lower limit on delay (i.e., phase shift) per decibel of power gain. It must be remembered, however, that one can usually trade delay for gain only by resorting to fairly complex circuitry, and thus the gain-bandwidth-product limitation implied by $\sigma_{\max}$ for circuits with indistinguishable delay and rise times (i.e. Eq. 3.63a) *is* of *practical* significance. Notice that in the case of feedback amplifiers the delay can be quite important and can prevent one from achieving large loop gains over a wide band of frequencies. Usually $\sigma_{\max}$ is less than $\omega_{\max}$, so this limitation is quite important.

3.2.3 *More General s-Plane Restrictions*

The $\omega_{\max}$ and $\sigma_{\max}$ limitations can be extended to a more general s-plane restriction on the real part of the complex power. Figure 3.23 shows a typical s-plane region in which P_R can be negative, and $\omega_{\max}$ and $\sigma_{\max}$ are seen to be only two parameters, which do not completely define the region. The more general restriction is: if U_a is U computed for the amplifier as a whole, and U_t is U for the transistor alone, then U_a can be greater than unity only for those frequencies for which $U_t > 1$. In short, the contour $U_t = 1$ in the complex plane delineates a portion of the right half of the s-plane, and only in this region can the amplifier produce useful power gain.

There are additional restrictions imposed by limitations on $P_I = I_m[P]$. For $s = j\omega$, L and C components can absorb either polarity of P_I, so the conditions for possible oscillation do not involve P_I. Likewise, for $s = \sigma$, $P_I = 0$, and is therefore unimportant. However, for complex s with $\sigma > 0$ the restriction on P_I may imply important gain-speed limitations.

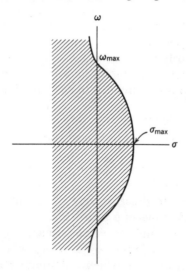

Fig. 3.23. Typical s-plane region for $\mathrm{Re}[P] < 0$.

Unfortunately, the more general s-plane power restrictions are computationally relatively difficult to apply. Moreover, the two parameters ω_{max} and σ_{max} are usually adequate to determine the important transistor limitations. Roughly speaking, ω_{max} describes a limitation on gain-bandwidth capabilities while σ_{max} describes a limitation on gain-per-unit delay capabilities.

3.3 SPEED LIMITATIONS UNDER LARGE-SIGNAL CONDITIONS

3.3.0 *Introduction*

The first part of this chapter has dealt solely with small-signal limitations on linear amplifiers. In other words, we have derived limitations which express the fact that when we have a limited amount of *signal* power with which to control a larger amount of *output* power, there are limitations on realizable delay and bandwidth.

We now come to the discussion of a class of limitations which are related only to the *bias power* (i.e., the power available from the dc supplies used in the amplifier) and which limit the speed in a way which is almost independent of gain or impedance considerations. This type of limitation is particularly important in the output stages of linear amplifiers or in switching circuits. It should be emphasized that in future discussions the term "large-signal" does not necessarily imply a nonlinear mode of operation. In many instances the large-signal limitations are a set of constraints which must be satisfied if the circuit is to *avoid* nonlinear operation.

3.3.1 dv/dt Limitations

A capacitor is described by the relation

$$i = C \frac{dv}{dt} \tag{3.65}$$

This simple relation describes one of the most important large-signal speed limitations of a transistor.

Consider, for example, a common-base amplifier as shown in Fig. 3.24. Assume that prior to $t = 0$, $v_{CB} = V_1$; but that at $t = 0$ we wish to supply an input which will produce the quickest possible change in output from V_1 to a new level, V_2. What is the minimum time T required to make this change? Note that we have specified a willingness to use *any* input which will achieve our desired goal; hence gain is not a consideration.

If V_2 is greater than V_1, the fastest possible response occurs if we supply an impulse of current to the emitter which is sufficient to reverse-bias the emitter and thereby turn off the transistor. In short, our optimum strategy is to let the full power of the $V_{CC} - R$ circuit be applied to charge up capacity $C\mu$. At such time that $V_{CB} = V_2$ we should turn the transistor back on, to prevent a continued rise in v_{CB}. The complete response would then be as shown in Fig. 3.25 and for C_μ constant the response time T is given by

$$T = RC_\mu \ln\left(\frac{V_{CC} - V_1}{V_{CC} - V_2}\right) \tag{3.66}$$

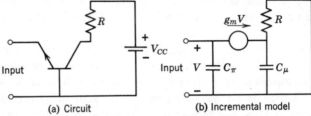

(a) Circuit   (b) Incremental model

Fig. 3.24. Common-base amplifier circuit.

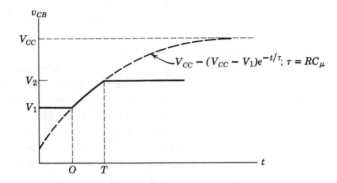

Fig. 3.25. Fastest possible rise-time for circuit in Fig. 3.24.

Note that the time T is governed by several parameters and is large for V_2 near V_{CC}.

The easiest way to express this limitation is to say that if $I_C = I_o$ before $t = 0$, the fastest possible rate of rise of v_{CB} after $t = 0$ is

$$\left(\frac{dv_{CB}}{dt}\right)_{\max} = \frac{I_o}{C_\mu} \tag{3.67}$$

The only way to increase the *rate of rise* of v_{CB} is to increase the quiescent bias current, I_o, or decrease C_μ by using a different transistor.

For $V_2 < V_1$ the transistor can, in principle, be driven far into conduction and the rate of fall of v_{CB} is limited only by the maximum current we are willing to pass through the transistor. It is conceivable that a practical circuit could achieve fall times which are less than 10% of the rise time, at which point the need for power gain may be the controlling factor in limiting speed.

This example illustrates two important ideas for large-signal operation: (1) the $\omega_{\max}$ gain-bandwidth limitations derived in Sec. 3.2 may be less important than I_o/C rate-of-rise limitations expressed by Eq. 3.67; and (2) the rise time may be considerably greater than the fall time (or vice versa).

Note that the best transistor to use for large-signal amplification in a circuit such as Fig. 3.24, is a transistor with a high current capability per unit of base-collector capacity. A typical transistor might be able to handle 200 ma with $C_\mu = 5$ pf, so $(dv_{CB}/dt)_{\max} = 40$ volts/nanosecond. Actually, of course, the current a transistor can pass will depend on the voltage, since the power rating will probably be the important limitation.

The preceding example illustrated large-signal rise and fall time limitations. Similar limitations also exist for large-signal sinusoidal operation, as can be seen in the following example. Let us suppose that the circuit of Fig. 3.24 is to be used to drive one deflection plate of a cathode ray tube. We will assume that the capacitance to ground of the deflection plate is C and that we require a sinusoidal component of collector voltage of magnitude $2V_p$ volts peak-to-peak. Also assume that the transistor has a maximum power rating of $\overline{v_{CB}i_C} \leq P_C$, and let us attempt to find the highest frequency that this amplifier can handle and still produce the desired output. In order to simplify the problem, we shall replace V_{CC} and R by a current source, I_o, which we will later adjust for "best" high frequency operation. This circuit is shown in Fig. 3.26a, and we shall assume that *any* emitter signal can be applied to produce the desired output. In the figure, C_μ is drawn external to the transistor, and i_C' is defined as that component of collector current which does not flow through C_μ. If the transistor is biased at (I_o, V_p), then the collector voltage waveform is of the form

$$v_{CB} = V_p + V_p \sin \omega t \tag{3.68}$$

assuming that the minimum possible value of v_{CB} is approximately zero. The capacitor current is

$$i_{\text{cap}} = (C_\mu + C)\,\frac{dv_{CB}}{dt} = V_p(C_\mu + C)\omega \cos \omega t$$

Hence the current i_C' is

$$i_C' = I_o - i_{\text{cap}} = I_o - V_p(C_\mu + C)\omega \cos \omega t \tag{3.69}$$

The v_{CB} voltage waveform will be as shown in Fig. 3.26b. The corresponding path of operation in the $i_C' - v_{CB}$ plane is shown in Fig. 3.26c. At low frequencies the path is a straight line, indicating that $i_C' = I_o$ (i.e., no capacitor current) and at high frequencies the path becomes elliptical. At the maximum frequency of operation, $\omega = \omega_{\text{MAX}}$, the current just goes to zero at one instant of each cycle. Hence, from Eq. 3.69, the frequency limitation is

$$\omega_{\text{MAX}} = \frac{I_o}{V_p(C_\mu + C)} \tag{3.70}$$

a result very similar in form to Eq. 3.67 above.

The maximum frequency of operation can also be expressed in terms of the average power rating P_C (based on a 1 millisecond

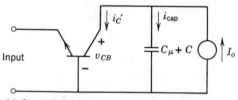

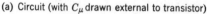

(a) Circuit (with C_μ drawn external to transistor)

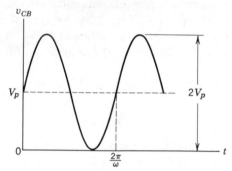

(b) Collector voltage waveform

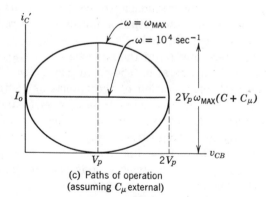

(c) Paths of operation
(assuming C_μ external)

Fig. 3.26. Common-base amplifier illustrating large-signal limitations on ω.

averaging time). If the frequency were always going to be much higher than 1 kc, then we would operate at maximum dissipation by setting $P_C = V_p I_o$. However, if we assume that the frequency might be much lower than 1 kc, then the limit must be applied to the peak power, which at low frequencies is, from Fig. 3.26c, $2V_p I_o$. Hence we set

$$P_C = 2V_p I_o \tag{3.71}$$

Eliminating I_o between Eqs. 3.70 and 3.71, we obtain

$$\omega_{\text{MAX}} = \frac{P_C}{2V_p{}^2(C + C_\mu)} = \frac{P_C}{W_{\text{peak}}} \tag{3.72}$$

where W_{peak} is the peak energy stored in the capacitors. Equation 3.72 gives us the maximum possible sinusoidal frequency that can be amplified by the circuit of Fig. 3.26. As typical numbers we might use $C = C_\mu = 5$ pf, $P_C = 8$ watts and $V_p = 20$ volts. From Eq. 3.70 we see that I_o is limited to 0.2 amperes and from Eq. 3.70

$$\omega_{\text{MAX}} = \frac{0.2}{20 \times 10^{-11}} = 10^9 \text{ rad/sec}$$

or

$$f_{\text{MAX}} = 160 \text{ mc/sec}$$

Making allowance for normal margins so that the transistor will not burn up for reasonable circuit variations, we would do well to achieve a maximum frequency of 100 mc/sec. The transistor may have considerable gain for frequencies above 100 mc, but the large-signal limitations require the output amplitude to be reduced if a pure sinusoidal output is desired.

An alternate interpretation of the large-signal limitation can be seen from the path of operation shown in Fig. 3.26c. The ellipse represents the path of operation of the transistor (with C_μ considered as part of the external circuit) for $\omega = \omega_{\text{MAX}}$ and the area of the ellipse is proportional to the ac *reactive* power supplied to the capacitors. Clearly high frequencies imply a large area ellipse and hence a large $V_p I_o$ product for linear operation. The speed limitation is really a limit on the reactive power that the transistor can supply to the load.

Notice that if we had required a peak-to-peak output voltage of 10 volts instead of 40 volts, the value of ω_{MAX} would be increased from 100 mc/sec to 1600 mc/sec. The large-signal limitation would then probably not be as serious as the small-signal limitations. For most circuits, if we gradually increase the magnitude of the output voltage we will, at some point, find that the speed of response is determined primarily by the circuit, and not by the driving signal.

It might be well to note that, if we altered the circuit of Fig. 3.24 to a common-emitter amplifier, the same ω_{MAX} limitations would apply. In fact, virtually all of the C_μ current would have to flow through the base lead. Figure 3.27 shows a model for the circuit of Fig. 3.24 with emitter and base interchanged. The fastest rate of rise of V_{CE} occurs for $i_{C}' = 0$ and the input current must be at least as large as $C_\mu(dv_{CB}/dt)$ in order to keep the transistor cut off. In order to achieve the maximum frequency capabilities, the driving amplifier must supply a signal current which is at least as large as the current through C_μ, and hence the output transistor does not really produce significant high-frequency current gain unless most of the capacitive load is external to the transistor. The common-base output stage is thus almost as good as the common-emitter from the point of view of high-frequency gain for large voltage swings, and may actually be better from the point of view of high breakdown voltage and a more constant current gain versus frequency characteristic.

3.3.2 *di/dt Limitations*

It is clear that, if inductive energy storage is dominant, we could have *di/dt* limitations exactly analogous to the *dv/dt* limitations examined in the preceding discussion. Normally, however, the important inductive energy storage is external to the transistor and the limitation takes on a slightly different form. To illustrate

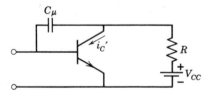

Fig. 3.27. Model for circuit of Fig. 3.24*a* in a common-emitter form.

this type of limitation we will consider the example of a transistor driving the deflection coil of a magnetically deflected cathode-ray tube.

The assumed circuit and required waveforms are shown in Fig. 3.28. In order to "flux up" the inductor in time T_1, we must have $V_{CC} = LI_m/T_1$ (assuming v_{CE} can be made negligibly small in comparison with V_{CC}). In order to discharge the inductor in time T_2, the peak value of v_{CE} will be $(v_{CE})_{\max} = V_{CC}T/T_2$. Since the inductive energy is $W_L = \frac{1}{2}LI_m{}^2$, we see that the power dissipated by the transistor is

$$\overline{(i_C \cdot v_{CE})} = \frac{W_L}{T} = fW_L \qquad (3.73a)$$

$$(i_C \cdot v_{CE})_{\max} = \frac{2W_L}{T_2} \qquad (3.73b)$$

It is typical that for a transistor driving a reactive load the average power dissipation capabilities must be at least as large as the product of the frequency times the peak energy stored in the reactance (Eq. 3.73a). It is also clear that the *peak* dissipation may be

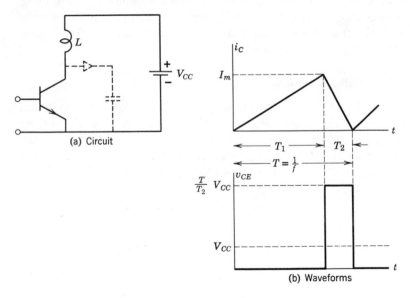

Fig. 3.28. Deflection-coil amplifier.

substantially larger than the average dissipation and the important limitation may, in fact, turn out to be at least partly a constraint on peak power.

If the collector current waveform is always the same, such as in a television horizontal deflection system, then we do not really have to dissipate $W_L f$ watts in the transistor. We could, for example, connect a capacitor-diode rectifier circuit, as shown by the dotted circuit in Fig. 3.28, to the collector of the transistor and recover the energy stored in the inductor. In actual fact, it is common to drive the deflection coil through a transformer and use a secondary winding on this transformer to develop a pulse of high voltage which is rectified and used as the electron beam accelerating voltage.

In some cases, however, the application requires the inductive current to be responsive to changes in input voltage and it becomes difficult, practically, to recover the stored energy and not dissipate it in the transistor. In principle it is not impossible to recover the energy, but except in very high power applications it may be impractical. We can, however, use quasi-linear amplifiers (see TCM*) to increase the $W_L f$ product without increasing the dissipation.

As an important concluding thought, we might observe that supplying energy to be stored in L or C may be at least as difficult as supplying energy to be dissipated in a resistor. The ratio of energy stored in the load to available output power sets a lower limit to how long it takes to change the load voltage and current.

PROBLEMS

P3.1 (a) Compute ω_{max} for an active device (e.g., a tunnel diode) which can be described by the linear model ($r, l, g, c \geq 0$) shown in Fig. 3.29.

   (b) What values of G, L, and C are needed to produce oscillations at $\omega = \omega_{max}$?

   (c) What is σ_{max} for this device?

P3.2 Compute ω_{max} and σ_{max} for the transistor models shown in Fig. 3.30.

*R. D. Thornton, J. G. Linvill, E. R. Chenette, H. L. Ablin, J. N. Harris, A. R. Boothroyd, and J. Willis, *Handbook of Basic Transistor Circuits and Measurements*, Wiley, New York, 1966.

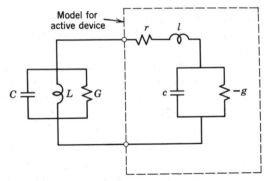

Fig. 3.29

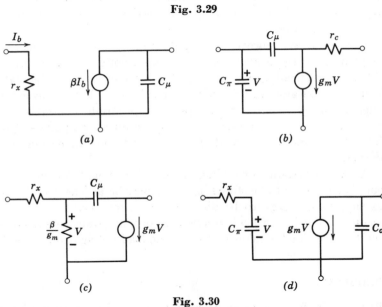

Fig. 3.30

P3.3   Assume that a transistor amplifier and its limitations are described by:

$$G_V = \left(\frac{G_{V0}\omega_{h1}}{s + \omega_{h1}}\right)^n; \quad |G_V| \leq 1 \text{ for } \sigma = \sigma_{max} \text{ and } \omega = \omega_{max}$$

(a) If you desire the amplifier to have the maximum possible bandwidth which is consistent with a specified $G_0 = G_{V0}^n$, what values of G_{V0}, ω_{h1}, and n would you use and what would be the resulting bandwidth?

(b) If you desire $|\underline{/G_V}| \leq \pi/2$ when $|G_V| \geq 1$, what is the largest frequency at which you can achieve $|G_V| = G_0$?

P3.4 Find a transformer network which converts the model of Fig. 3.13 into a negative resistance, $-r$, in parallel with a capacitance, C. Adjust the turns ratio to maximize the rC product and compare this product with what you know is the limit based on a σ_{max} calculation.

P3.5 Assume a negative resistance, $-r$, has associated shunt capacitance, C, and show that $\sigma_{max} = (rC)^{-1}$. Any power amplifier constructed by connecting this negative resistor between the source and load, must have limitations on power gain and bandwidth.

    (a) Express these limitations in terms of σ_{max}.

    (b) Find a circuit which achieves the "best" possible bandwidth for a specified gain.

    (c) If a circuit contains this negative resistance element plus ideal resistors, inductors, and capacitors, what natural frequencies are possible?

P3.6 Derive Eq. 3.63a.

P3.7 Derive σ_{max} for the model of Fig. 3.22 without neglecting g_b, g_c, and g_d.

P3.8 Show that ω_{MAX} for the circuit of Fig. 3.24 (i.e., Fig. 3.26 with I_o replaced by V_{CC} and R) is the same as ω_{MAX} in Eq. 3.72 except that the factor 2 is replaced by $9/4\sqrt{3} = 1.30$. To do this, first show that the optimum parameter choices are $V_{CC} = 3V_p$ and $R = 9V_p{}^2/4P_C$.

P3.9 A dc amplifier has iterated, unilateral stages each with a single-pole response. The per-stage power gain is A_{01}^2 and the per-stage frequency response has the form of Eq. 3.4 with bandwidth ω_{h1}. For n stages the power gain is $A_{0n}^2 = A_{01}^{2n}$ and the bandwidth is $\omega_{hn} \approx \omega_{h1} (\ln 2/n)^{1/2}$ (see MTC, Sec. 8.2.2). Show that if $\omega_{h1}A_{01} = \tau_{min}^{-1}$, then for a given overall power gain A_0^2 and bandwidth ω_h, there is a bandwidth limitation

$$\omega_h \leq (e\tau_{min} \ln A_0^2)^{-1/2} = 0.61\tau_{min}^{-1}(\ln A_0^2)^{-1/2}$$

and that maximum bandwidth occurs for $A_{01}^2 = e$.

4

Noise

4.0 INTRODUCTION

"Noise" is a term used to signify extraneous signals which do not convey any useful information for the problem at hand, and which can only be described by their statistical properties. There are several physical mechanisms which can cause noise, but for transistors the important mechanisms all hinge on the discrete nature of the electronic charge. For frequencies above a few kilocycles per second (depending on the device and operating point), the mean-square noise amplitude can usually be predicted accurately on the basis of relatively simple circuit models. If we understand the characteristics of noise sources, we can design circuits which minimize their effect, and thereby achieve low-noise transistor amplifiers.

The intent of this chapter is to explain the physical mechanisms which cause noise, to develop circuit models which display the noise sources inherent in a transistor, and to indicate methods of minimizing noise. First, however, some analytical methods will be developed and applied to the idealized *pn* junction diode.

Except for the derivations of Johnson noise and shot noise in diodes and transistors, all discussions in Sections 4.1 to 4.4 will be in terms of voltages and currents as a function of time (i.e., time-domain representation). This is accomplished by assuming all networks to be resistive. In Section 4.5 this restriction is removed, and methods of handling noise sources in frequency-dependent networks are presented.

4.1 ANALYSIS INVOLVING NOISE SOURCES

4.1.1 *Introduction*

Noise sources are unpredictable in the sense that instantaneous waveforms can not be predicted over any significant interval of time. One can, however, describe noise sources in statistical terms, such as probabilities, mean-square values, and correlation functions. This section introduces very briefly a few important methods of dealing with these ideas.

4.1.2 *Addition of Noise Sources*

Assume that $v_1(t)$ and $v_2(t)$ are two noise sources and that $v_s(t)$ is the sum $v_1(t) + v_2(t)$. Consider the problem of expressing the mean-square value of $v_s(t)$ in terms of the mean-square values of $v_1(t)$ and $v_2(t)$. We shall use the notation:

$$\overline{v^2(t)} \equiv \text{mean-square value of } v \qquad (4.1)$$

Thus we have:

$$\overline{v_s{}^2(t)} = \overline{[v_1(t) + v_2(t)]^2} = \overline{v_1{}^2(t)} + \overline{v_2{}^2(t)} + \overline{2v_1(t)v_2(t)}$$

The mean-square value of v_s can also be written

$$\overline{v_s{}^2(t)} = \overline{v_1{}^2(t)} + \overline{v_2{}^2(t)} + 2C_{12}\left|\overline{[v_1{}^2(t)v_2{}^2(t)]}^{1/2}\right| \qquad (4.2)$$

where

$$C_{12} \equiv \frac{\overline{v_1(t)v_2(t)}}{\left|\overline{[v_1{}^2(t)v_2{}^2(t)]}^{1/2}\right|} = \text{correlation coefficient}$$

The coefficient C_{12} is a measure of the correlation between v_1 and v_2 and always lies in the range $-1 \leq C_{12} \leq 1$. Two sources are said to be uncorrelated if $C_{12} = 0$. It is quite common for two noise sources to be uncorrelated and this feature can greatly simplify noise analysis.

Note that from Eq. 4.2 two series-connected, uncorrelated voltage sources will have heating effects which are additive. That is, the power delivered to a resistor by the two together can be computed as the sum of the powers which would be delivered to the resistor by each source acting separately. The above result can be extended by superposition to apply to the effect of uncorrelated noise sources located anywhere in a linear network. Thus, interpreting $v_1(t)$ and $v_2(t)$ as voltages produced across some resistor in the network by separate action of two uncorrelated sources, we see that the noise power delivered to this element is the sum of the power delivered by each uncorrelated noise source acting separately.

As a word of caution, it is not by any means always easy to tell whether two noise sources are uncorrelated. Two sources caused by independent physical mechanisms are, of course, uncorrelated. However, the sources may also be uncorrelated even when caused by the *same* physical mechanism.

4.1.3 *Spectral Density**

The voltage wave from a noise source $v(t)$ will contain a great many frequency components. To indicate how these components are distributed as a function of frequency, we plot what is called the *spectral density*, a graph versus frequency of *mean-square noise voltage per unit bandwidth*. This graph might be obtained by feeding the source into a filter which passes unattenuated all frequencies in a band Δf centered at f_o, and completely rejects all other frequencies. The *mean-square value* of the filter output voltage is $S(f_o)\Delta f$, where $S(f_o)$ is the spectral density at the frequency f_o.

Because the ordinary Fourier transform for a random signal is not defined (because it does not, in general, yield convergent integrals), we cannot use conventional Fourier techniques to find the spectral density of the noise. Instead, we must first form the *autocorrelation function* of $v(t)$, defined as†

$$R(\tau) = \lim_{T \to \infty} \frac{1}{2T} \int_{-T}^{T} v(t)v(t + \tau)\, dt \qquad (4.3)$$

* The derivations in Secs. 4.1.3 and 4.2.1 can be omitted if the reader is willing to accept Eqs. 4.9 and 4.11 without proof.
† See, for example, W. B. Davenport and W. L. Root, *Random Signals and Noise*, McGraw-Hill, 1958.

The spectral density is then by definition the Fourier transform $W(f)$ of the autocorrelation function $R(\tau)$. That is,

$$W(f) \equiv \int_{-\infty}^{\infty} R(\tau)e^{-j2\pi f\tau}\, d\tau \qquad (4.4a)$$

For real time functions, $R(\tau)$ is a real, even function of τ. Thus, $W(f)$ can be written as

$$W(f) = \int_{-\infty}^{\infty} R(\tau)\cos 2\pi f\tau\, d\tau \qquad (4.4b)$$

It is clear from Eq. 4.4b that because $R(\tau)$ is real, $W(f)$ is a real, even function of f; that is, $W(f) = W(-f)$.

The corresponding inverse Fourier transform relation between $R(\tau)$ and $W(f)$ is

$$R(\tau) = \int_{-\infty}^{\infty} W(f)e^{j2\pi\tau f}\, df = \int_{-\infty}^{\infty} W(f)\cos 2\pi\tau f\, df \qquad (4.5)$$

The spectral density $W(f)$, defined above, is a "two-sided" representation; that is, it is defined in terms of both positive and negative frequency. However, by convention in noise analysis, the spectral density is defined in terms of positive frequency only (i.e., "one-sided"). Because of the fact that $W(f) = W(-f)$, as shown above, conversion from the two-sided representation to the one-sided spectral density, designated here as $S(f)$, involves nothing more than multiplying by a factor of two to account for the contributions of $W(f)$ at negative frequencies. Specifically, Eq. 4.5 becomes

$$R(\tau) = \int_{-\infty}^{\infty} W(f)\cos 2\pi\tau f\, df$$

$$= 2\int_{0}^{\infty} W(f)\cos 2\pi\tau f\, df$$

$$= \int_{0}^{\infty} S(f)\cos 2\pi\tau f\, df \qquad (4.5a)$$

and Eq. 4.4b becomes

$$S(f) = 2W(f) \qquad (f \geq 0)$$

$$= 2\int_{-\infty}^{\infty} R(\tau)\cos 2\pi f\tau\, d\tau \qquad (f \geq 0) \qquad (4.6)$$

In terms of $S(f)$, the spectral density for positive frequencies only, we have for $\tau = 0$ in Eq. 4.5a,

$$R(0) = \int_0^\infty S(f)\, df \qquad (4.7)$$

However, from Eq. 4.3,

$$R(0) = \lim_{T \to \infty} \frac{1}{2T} \int_{-T}^{T} v^2(t)\, dt = \overline{v(t)^2} \qquad (4.8)$$

By eliminating $R(0)$ from Eqs. 4.7 and 4.8, we arrive at an important relation called Parseval's theorem:

$$\overline{v(t)^2} = \int_0^\infty S(f)\, df \qquad (4.9)$$

If we consider that the voltage v is developed across a 1-ohm resistor, then Eq. 4.9 states the obvious fact that the average power in the noise signal must be the same as the power in its spectrum (the area under the spectral density curve).

4.2 NOISE IN A *pn* JUNCTION DIODE

4.2.1 *Shot Noise in Reverse Bias*

If a *pn* junction is several volts back-biased, then, roughly speaking, all of the minority carriers within one diffusion length of the junction will move by diffusion into the space-charge region and then be attracted across it by the high electric field. These carriers create a current; but, because of the discrete nature of the electronic charge, the current will appear to a first approximation as a series of impulses of area q as indicated in Fig. 4.1a. The time at which any one carrier traverses the junction is statistically independent of the time that any other carrier traverses the junction, and thus the current pulses can be assumed to be completely independent of one another. As stated in Sec. 4.1.3, we find the spectral density of this current waveform by finding first the autocorrelation function, defined in this case as

$$R(\tau) = \lim_{T \to \infty} \frac{1}{2T} \int_{-T}^{T} i(t)i(t + \tau)\, dt \qquad (4.10)$$

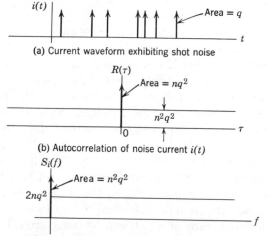

(a) Current waveform exhibiting shot noise

(b) Autocorrelation of noise current $i(t)$

(c) Spectral density versus f, assuming n uncorrelated pulses per second

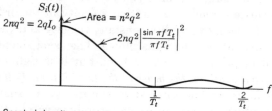

(d) Waveform for very low current

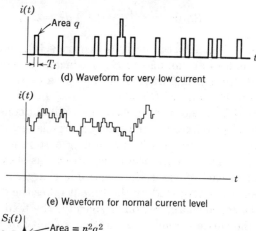

(e) Waveform for normal current level

(f) Spectral density versus f, assuming n uncorrelated pulses per second

Fig. 4.1 Shot noise in a back-biased pn junction diode. (a,b,c,) First approximation assuming current impulses. (d,e,f) Second approximation assuming current pulses of length T_t.

For $\tau = 0$, the autocorrelation will have an impulse of area nq^2 where n is the average number of pulses per second. To compute $R(\tau)$ for any other value of τ, recall that for two independent time waveforms, the average of the product of the two waves is the same as the product of their averages. Thus, because in this problem the current pulses are completely independent, the autocorrelation for $\tau \neq 0$ will be constant, equal to the square of the dc value of the current, as shown in Fig. 4.1*b*.

The spectral density of the current, $S_i(\omega)$, will be the Fourier transform of this $R(\tau)$. This transformation can best be done by splitting $R(\tau)$ into two parts: $R_a(\tau)$, the impulse, and $R_b(\tau)$, the constant value. The impulse $R_a(\tau)$ transforms to a constant value in $S_i(\omega)$, the magnitude of which can be found from Eq. 4.6 with $f = 0$.

$$S_{ia}(0) = 2 \int_{-\infty}^{\infty} R_a(\tau) \, d\tau = 2nq^2$$

as shown in Fig. 4.1*c*. Similarly (or conversely), the constant $R_b(\tau)$ transforms into an impulse in $S_i(\omega)$ which represents the dc component of the current waveform. The area of the impulse can be found from Eq. 4.5*a* with $\tau = 0$.

In actual fact, the current waveform will not consist of impulses. When an electron crosses the space-charge layer, it induces a current waveform more closely resembling a square pulse. Thus the current $i(t)$ can be more accurately drawn as shown in Fig. 4.1*d*. The area of each pulse is the electronic charge, q, and the width of the pulse is determined by the time it takes the electron to move across the space-charge region. Typically, the field is large enough so that the carriers reach a saturation velocity in the order of 10^7 cm/sec. Thus they move with a constant velocity and the current pulse is approximately square, as shown. The exact shape of these pulses is not of prime importance here, but it is significant that *the pulses have a width on the order of the transit time T_t through the space-charge layer.* In the interest of simplicity, we shall neglect any carriers which are generated or recombine within the space-charge region.

If the current and transit time are small, the current waveform would appear as shown in Fig. 4.1*d*. For normal currents, however, there will be many carriers in transit at a given time, and thus the pulses will pile up on top of one another, as shown in Fig. 4.1*e*.

However, the important facts are (1) the time at which any one carrier traverses the junction is statistically independent of the time that any other carrier traverses the junction, and (2) the velocity with which the carriers move is virtually independent of how many carriers there are in the space-charge region. Thus the current pulses in Fig. 4.1e can still be assumed to be completely independent.

The spectral density of this waveform is shown in Fig. 4.1f. We shall not attempt to derive this result here, because in fact the detailed shape of this spectrum is not germane to the present discussion. Suffice is it to say that the waveform in Fig. 4.1d can be obtained by convolving the waveform in Fig. 4.1a with a square pulse of length T_t and height $1/T_t$. The methods developed in Sec. 4.5, show that convolution in the time domain (Eq. 4.59) by a square pulse corresponds to multiplication of the spectrum by

$$|H(f)|^2 = \frac{\sin^2 \pi f T_t}{(\pi f T_t)^2}$$

(see Eq. 4.62).

From Fig. 4.1f we note that except for the dc component which does not concern us here, the spectral density has a relatively constant value of $2nq^2$ out to a frequency $f = 1/10T_t$. Typically this frequency is of the order of f_T or above. Thus we can consider the spectral density of the noise to be flat for all frequencies of interest in transistor circuits, i.e., below f_T. In all subsequent calculations in this chapter, we shall make this assumption, recognizing of course that for some unusually high-frequency transistors a more careful calculation may have to be made of the noise at extremely high frequencies.

On the basis that the dc current flowing through the diode is $\overline{i(t)} = I_o = nq$, we are led to the important conclusion that the spectral density of shot noise in a reverse-biased *pn* junction is virtually constant at a value

$$S_i(f) = 2qI_o \qquad (4.11a)$$

for $f > 0$ (see Problem P4.1).

In fact, all shot noise is characterized by discrete charge carriers crossing a region. If I is the average current flowing in the process, then the shot noise spectral density is

$$S_i(f) = 2qI \qquad (4.11b)$$

If the noise spectral density is given by Eq. 4.11*b*, then the current I is said to cause "full shot noise." Note that there are three conditions which must be satisfied for full shot noise to exist: (*1*) the charge on each carrier must be the same; (*2*) the frequency range of interest must be small compared with the inverse transit time of the carrier across the junction; and (*3*) the motion of any one carrier must be statistically independent of the motion of all other carriers. As an example, the dc bias currents in a transistor tend to exhibit full shot noise, and this is one of the most important sources of noise in a transistor.

4.2.2 *Shot Noise for Forward Bias*

For a forward bias, we can resolve the diode current into two physically distinct components. On the basis of the diode equation

$$I = I_o(e^{qV/kT} - 1) \tag{4.12}$$

these components are

$$I_1 = -I_o \tag{4.13}$$

$$I_2 = I_o e^{qV/kT} \tag{4.14}$$

where I_1 is the reverse saturation current arising from thermally-generated minority carriers on each side, and I_2 arises from the diffusion of majority carriers against the potential barrier on each side. Whereas the average values of these currents tend to oppose each other in the total current, the noise components associated with these currents, being uncorrelated, will add in a mean-square sense. Thus according to the full-shot-noise results in Fig. 4.1 and Eq. 4.11, we have at low enough frequencies

$$S_i(f) = 2qI_o + 2qI_o e^{qV/kT}$$
$$= 2qI_o(e^{qV/kT} + 1) \tag{4.15a}$$

The frequency limit of this result is again set by the transit time of carriers across the space-charge layer, but of course this time will not be the same in forward bias as in reverse bias.

By using Eq. 4.12, we can reduce Eq. 4.15*a* to

$$S_i(f) = 2q[2I_o + I] \tag{4.15b}$$

Under reverse-bias conditions, $I = -I_o$, and Eq. 4.15b becomes $S_i(f) = 2qI_o$, in agreement with Eq. 4.11a. For large forward bias, I is much larger than I_o, and $S_i(f)$ becomes approximately

$$S_i(f) \cong 2qI$$

$$= 2kTg \qquad (4.16)$$

where g is the incremental conductance at the operating point

$$g \equiv \frac{\partial I}{\partial V} \cong \frac{q}{kT} I$$

We thus conclude that a strongly forward-biased pn junction exhibits the full shot noise associated with its average current.

In zero bias, and therefore with the junction *in thermal equilibrium*, the two currents I_1 and I_2 in Eqs. 4.13 and 4.14 cancel on the average, but their noise components are still independent, and add in a mean square sense. On this basis, the current across the junction appears as shown in Fig. 4.2a. So from Eq. 4.15 we find (see also Fig. 4.2b) for low enough frequencies the spectral density

$$S_i(f) = 4qI_o \qquad (4.17)$$

Thus, the noise is identical to shot noise associated with a dc current twice as large as the reverse saturation current of the diode. Since, in fact, there is no dc current flowing under the assumed zero-bias conditions, it is convenient to eliminate I_o from Eq. 4.17 by rewriting it in terms of the incremental diode conductance. On differentiating Eq. 4.12, we obtain

$$g_o = \frac{dI}{dV}\bigg|_{V=0} = \frac{I_o q}{kT} ; \quad \text{or} \quad I_o = \frac{kTg_o}{q} \qquad (4.18)$$

Thus Eq. 4.17 becomes

$$S_i(f) = 4kTg_o \qquad (4.19)$$

For small variations of V about $V = 0$, we can make a time-domain Norton equivalent circuit to portray the noise and the V-I relation. Such a model is shown in Fig. 4.2c. The noise source $i_n(t)$ is, by definition, the short-circuit noise current waveform, and has the spectral density given in Fig. 4.2b.

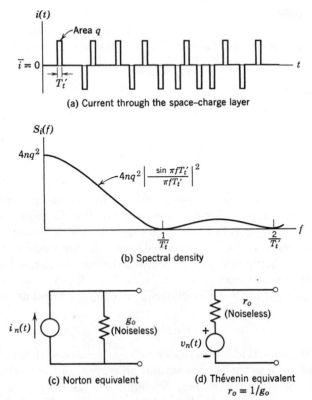

(a) Current through the space–charge layer

(b) Spectral density

(c) Norton equivalent

(d) Thévenin equivalent
$r_o = 1/g_o$

Fig. 4.2 Shot noise in pn junction diode under zero-bias conditions.

If we were to measure the mean-square value of the short-circuit current flowing at the terminals of the noise model, Fig. 4.2c, the result would be, from Eqs. 4.9 and 4.19,

$$\overline{i_n^2(t)} = \int_f^{f+\Delta f} S_i(f)\, df$$

$$\cong 4kTg_o\, \Delta f \tag{4.20}$$

where, for simplicity, we have assumed that the measuring instrument passes all frequencies over some band Δf, and rejects all other frequencies. (What would be measured by a real instrument with gradual rather than sharp band edges can be determined by the methods of Sec. 4.5.)

Clearly the time-domain Thévenin equivalent noise model, Fig. 4.2*d*, has a voltage source with a mean-square value

$$\overline{v_n{}^2(t)} = 4kTr_o\,\Delta f \tag{4.21}$$

It follows from Eq. 4.21 that the spectral density of the noise voltage source $v_n(t)$ will have a value of

$$S_v(f) = 4kTr_o \tag{4.22}$$

over the entire range of interest to us. It is important to note that the values of the thermal-equilibrium noise sources in Figs. 4.2*c* and *d* depend only on kT and the incremental resistance of the diode.

4.2.3   Resistance Noise

If we connect a "noisy" diode under zero-bias *thermal equilibrium* conditions to a noiseless resistor, the diode noise source would cause heating of the noiseless resistor. However, if the resistor and diode are in thermal equilibrium at the same temperature, then we know from the second law of thermodynamics that there can be no net transfer of noise power between them, regardless of what frequency interval their contact may be limited to by imposing lossless filters between them. Thus we must conclude that *all resistors have associated noise sources*. The noise associated with a resistor at *thermal equilibrium* is called *resistance noise* or *Johnson noise*. It is not hard to show that if two resistors of values r_1 and r_2 (with Thévenin equivalent noise voltages $\overline{v_1{}^2} = 4kTr_1\Delta f$ and $\overline{v_2{}^2} = 4kTr_2\Delta f$) are connected together, there is no net transfer of noise power, and the second law is satisfied. Thus the models of Figs. 4.2*c* and 4.2*d* are valid for any linear or nonlinear element, provided only that it is in *thermal equilibrium at temperature* T, *and that it may be considered linear as far as the noise is concerned*.

Note that we have a choice of interpreting the noise of a diode at thermal equilibrium. We can think of it as shot noise associated with the independent flow of the two currents I_1 and I_2 (Eqs. 4.13 and 4.14), *or* we can consider the noise as "resistance noise" associated with the incremental diode resistance. These are simply two different ways of viewing the *same equilibrium motion*. In general, however, the shot noise concept involves fundamentally a *directed* motion with random transits, whereas the "resistance noise" or "equilibrium noise" idea involves motion which is random in *direction* as well as magnitude.

Our "derivation" of the Johnson noise (Eqs. 4.21 and 4.22) from considering a *pn* junction at zero bias appears to limit the result to frequencies for which the shot noise description of the component diode currents is valid. This implication is false. Resistance noise, or Johnson noise, should really be called *thermal equilibrium noise*, and is a very fundamental property of the fluctuation of thermodynamic systems in thermal equilibrium. The fact is that, on thermodynamic grounds, the available noise power from *any* dissipative system in thermal equilibrium at temperature T must be kT watts per cycle of measurement bandwidth (up to very high frequencies $\approx kT/h$). Accordingly our noise model for the *pn* junction under bias conditions would surely have been wrong if it had *not* reduced properly to Eqs. 4.21 and 4.22 at zero bias.

Notice, though, the interesting fact that the mean-square value of the *nonequilibrium* noise current in Eq. 4.16 is only one-half as large as we would expect in the same frequency interval from a resistor of value equal to the incremental diode resistance and in thermal equilibrium at the same temperature.

Aside from the junction, however, there are regions of a real diode which, although carrying the forward-bias current, are very nearly in thermal equilibrium. These regions exhibit Johnson noise (Eqs. 4.20 or 4.21), independent of the junction shot noise given by Eqs. 4.15. The temperature of these resistive regions may, of course, exceed that of the ambient because of joule heating; the Johnson noise is then based upon the local resistance and temperature of these regions.

4.2.4 *1/f Noise*

There is an important type of noise which has a spectral density roughly proportional to $1/f$. This type of noise will inevitably dominate at low frequencies, typically below about 1000 cps but sometimes extending well into the megacycle region. Unfortunately, this noise can not be predicted accurately and does not lend itself to physical analysis as readily as is the case for shot noise and resistance noise.

"$1/f$ noise," sometimes called *flicker noise*, is known to arise from the generation or recombination of carriers on the surface, although other physical processes can also produce it. For example, it can also arise as a result of temperature fluctuations. Note that only 0.001°C fluctuation in temperature can cause 2 to 3 microvolts of fluctuation in voltage across a forward-biased diode.

Although it is difficult to predict the amount of $1/f$ noise, it is, of course, always possible to measure $1/f$ noise for a particular device and then represent the measurement in a circuit model. Fortunately, it is usually true that the steps one takes to improve device quality, and to minimize shot and resistance noise, will also tend to minimize $1/f$ noise.

4.3 NOISE SOURCES IN A TRANSISTOR

The important noise mechanisms in a transistor are the same as those for a diode. The only new problem is to account properly for noise associated with two interacting junctions. The primary objective of this section is to develop circuit models suitable for calculating noise performance of small-signal transistor amplifiers. For simplicity of analysis, the development is based on common-emitter operation and is expressed in terms of noise generators in the hybrid-π model.

4.3.1 *Shot Noise Caused by dc Bias Currents*

We observed that for a *pn*-junction diode, we could attribute full shot noise to each distinct component of the current. Thus it is reasonable to expect that we can attribute full shot noise to each distinct component of the dc bias currents for a transistor. The chief problem is to be sure that we locate the shot noise generators at the proper place in the hybrid-π model and to establish what, if any, correlation exists between these generators.

We shall assume that the transistor is a *pnp* unit, whose dc characteristics are given by the Ebers-Moll relations.

$$I_E = I_{ES}[e^{qV_{EB}/kT} - 1] - \alpha_R I_{CS}[e^{qV_{CB}/kT} - 1]$$
$$I_C = -\alpha_F I_{ES}[e^{qV_{EB}/kT} - 1] + I_{CS}[e^{qV_{CB}/kT} - 1] \tag{4.23}$$

We assume, initially, that the transistor has unity emitter and collector efficiencies, so that *all* longitudinal current flow results from the motion of holes.

In order to find a noise model containing uncorrelated noise sources, we must resolve the various dc currents into physically distinct components, and then identify a separate noise generator for each distinguishable group of holes. As a start, Eq. 4.23 can be used to find expressions for I_E, I_C, and I_B, assuming the normal bias condition, $(qV_{CB}/kT) \ll -1$, and using the reciprocity relation, $\alpha_F I_{ES} = \alpha_R I_{CS}$. Thus we find:

$$I_E = \alpha_F I_{ES} e^{qV_{EB}/kT} + (1 - \alpha_F) I_{ES} e^{qV_{EB}/kT} - I_{ES}(1 - \alpha_F)$$
(4.24a)

$$I_C = -\alpha_F I_{ES} e^{qV_{EB}/kT} - I_{CS}(1 - \alpha_R)$$
(4.24b)

$$I_B = -(1 - \alpha_F) I_{ES} e^{qV_{EB}/kT} + I_{ES}(1 - \alpha_F) + I_{CS}(1 - \alpha_R)$$
(4.24c)

On the basis of Eqs. 4.24 we can identify four distinct current components:

$$I_1 = \alpha_F I_{ES} e^{qV_{EB}/kT}$$

$$I_2 = (1 - \alpha_F) I_{ES} e^{qV_{EB}/kT}$$

$$I_3 = I_{ES}(1 - \alpha_F)$$

$$I_4 = I_{CS}(1 - \alpha_R)$$

Then Eqs. 4.24 simplify to

$$I_E = I_1 + I_2 - I_3$$
(4.24d)

$$I_C = -I_1 - I_4$$
(4.24e)

$$I_B = -I_2 + I_3 + I_4$$
(4.24f)

Note that because α_F, α_R, I_{ES}, and I_{CS} are, by definition, positive numbers, I_1, I_2, I_3, and I_4 are always positive quantities.

The currents I_1, I_2, I_3, and I_4 can be interpreted in terms of a corpuscular charge flow picture as shown in Fig. 4.3a. The four groups of holes associated with currents I_1 to I_4 have the following physical identification:

I_1: Holes injected from the emitter into the base and collected by the collector. This is by far the largest group of holes.

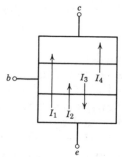

(a) Hole currents in an idealized *pnp* junction transistor

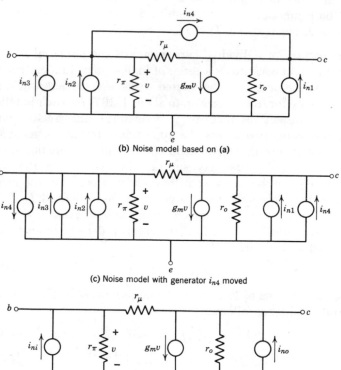

(b) Noise model based on (a)

(c) Noise model with generator i_{n4} moved

(d) Simplification of (c), assuming $|I_C| \gg I_3 + I_4$

Fig. 4.3. Shot-noise models for a junction transistor, neglecting r_x.

I_2: Holes injected from the emitter into the base and which recombine in the base. These holes, together with those in group 1, are usually the most important ones.

I_3: Holes thermally generated in the base region and injected into the emitter region. We see from Eq. 4.24a that $-I_3$ is the emitter current that flows for $V_{EB} \ll 0$, i.e., both junctions reverse biased. The current which flows under this condition is clearly less than I_{EO}, a fact that can be understood from physical reasoning or by recalling that $I_{EO} = I_{ES}(1 - \alpha_F \alpha_R)$, and thus $I_3 < I_{EO}$.

I_4: Holes thermally generated in the base region and injected into the collector region. This is the collector current that flows when both junctions are reverse-biased. For reasons analogous to those for I_3 given above, $I_4 < I_{CO}$.

The passage of individual carriers across the potential barriers of the junction constitutes a series of independent random events. Therefore, the dc current associated with these carriers will cause full shot noise for frequencies up to about $1/10T_t$ for each junction. We can represent the noise by four separate, uncorrelated noise generators connected across the appropriate terminals, as shown in Fig. 4.3b. Note that here, as in the case of the junction diode, certain dc components may subtract in making up the total current, but the shot noise contributions always *add* in the mean-square sense. To emphasize this point, we have defined I_1, I_2, I_3, and I_4 in such a way that they are *always positive quantities*.

We have already shown that the spectral density of shot noise associated with a current I is

$$S_i(f) = 2qI \tag{4.25}$$

Thus, on the basis of Eqs. 4.24, the noise sources in Fig. 4.3 have spectral densities as follows:

$$S_{i1}(f) = 2q\alpha_F I_{ES} e^{qV_{EB}/kT} \tag{4.26a}$$

$$S_{i2}(f) = 2q(1 - \alpha_F)I_{ES} e^{qV_{EB}/kT} \tag{4.26b}$$

$$S_{i3}(f) = 2qI_{ES}(1 - \alpha_F) \tag{4.26c}$$

$$S_{i4}(f) = 2qI_{CS}(1 - \alpha_R) \tag{4.26d}$$

For most purposes, however, we can make an approximation which eliminates the noise generator between base and collector.

First, we replace the generator i_{n4} by two equal generators, one between base and emitter and the other between emitter and collector, as shown in Fig. 4.3c. On the basis that the two i_{n4} generators in this figure are completely correlated, Fig. 4.3c is an exact replacement for Fig. 4.3b.

For normal transistor bias, $|I_C| \gg I_{CO}$. Under these conditions we can ignore i_{n4} in comparison with i_{n1} at the output, and represent the output noise by one source i_{no} of spectral density

$$S_{i(\text{output})} \cong S_{i1}(f) = 2q|I_1|$$
$$\cong 2q|I_C| \tag{4.27}$$

as shown in Fig. 4.3d. (It is desirable in our development to eliminate i_{n4} from the output noise source in order to get rid of correlation between input and output noise sources.)

The input noise source i_{ni} in Fig. 4.3d represents the combined effects of i_{n2}, i_{n3}, and i_{n4}. On the basis that these three sources are uncorrelated, the spectral density of i_{ni} is

$$S_{i(\text{input})} = 2q[I_2 + I_3 + I_4]$$
$$\equiv 2qI_B' \tag{4.28}$$

where, for convenience, we have defined I_B' as a *positive* number equal to

$$I_B' \equiv I_2 + I_3 + I_4$$

The two noise generators i_{ni} and i_{no} in Fig. 4.3d are then proportional to I_B' and $|I_C|$, respectively.

Alternatively, we can express the noise generators in terms of mean-square currents measured in a bandwidth Δf,

$$\overline{i_{ni}^2} = 2qI_B' \, \Delta f \tag{4.29}$$
$$\overline{i_{no}^2} = 2q|I_C| \, \Delta f \tag{4.30}$$

From Eq. 4.24f, we see that I_B' can also be written as

$$I_B' = -I_B + 2(I_3 + I_4) \tag{4.31a}$$
$$= -I_B + 2[I_{ES}(1 - \alpha_F) + I_{CS}(1 - \alpha_R)] \tag{4.31b}$$

Physically, $I_3 + I_4$ is the current caused by thermal generation in the base. Often we can neglect this term and assume $I_B' \cong -I_B$. However, in germanium transistors at low bias currents $I_3 + I_4$

may be significant. To the extent that the Ebers-Moll equations are valid, $I_3 + I_4$ is the total base current that flows when both emitter and collector junctions are reverse-biased.

It is clear from Eq. 4.28 or 4.29 that noise associated with $I_3 + I_4$ represents a minimum noise which cannot be reduced by simply operating at lower collector current levels. Thus, silicon transistors have a significant advantage over germanium units when low noise is desired with normal room temperature operation.

The expressions for the two noise generators are not changed if the model is generalized to include the flow of electrons. Also, the presence of a trapping recombination current at the emitter-base junction does not alter the model; this current also contributes full shot noise.

4.3.2 Base Resistance Noise

If the ohmic base resistance of a transistor were external to the active base region, then it would be a simple matter to represent its noise contribution. Assuming an extrinsic base resistance r_x, we would add a noise generator v_{nx} in series with the base lead as in Fig. 4.4a. The spectral density for this source would be constant at a value $S_{v(\text{extrinsic})} = 4kTr_x$. At moderately large bias levels, such a procedure is valid because most of the transistor action is near the periphery of the emitter region, and the extrinsic base resistance is more important than resistance within the active region. However, as we shall see, low-noise operation requires low bias currents, so it is important to account for the distributed nature of the base resistance.

Assume that the transistor has an emitter stripe geometry similar to that shown in Figs. 1.6 and 1.10a. For simplicity, we shall represent the transistor by the multilump model shown in Fig. 4.4b. This model assumes that the base is divided into n thin strips, and r_B is assumed to be the total layer resistance, as in Eq. 1.19b (page 29). Also, emitter crowding has been neglected. It does take much calculation to see that the model of Fig. 4.4a cannot properly represent the distributed base resistance indicated in Fig. 4.4b. The value of r_x which gives the correct input impedance does not, in general, give the correct value for the noise

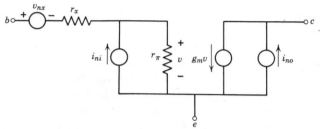

(a) Simple model, assuming r_x is extrinsic, and $r_\mu = r_o = \infty$

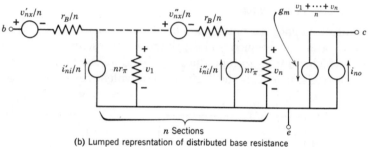

(b) Lumped represntation of distributed base resistance

Fig. 4.4. Noise models for a transistor.

generator. However, at low bias currents we can assume $r_\pi \gg r_B$ and, in this case, a straightforward calculation (see Problem P4.2) shows that if

$$r_x = r_B \frac{(n+1)(2n+1)}{6n^2}$$

then the models of Figs. 4.4a and 4.4b can be made to agree. For the distributed case where n approaches infinity, we thus have $r_x = r_B/3$ (which is in agreement with the results of PEM, Chapter 8).

Thus, for low and moderately large dc collector current levels, the model of Fig. 4.4a represents accurately the important noise sources in a transistor, provided that $1/f$ noise can be neglected (i.e., f greater than, roughly, 1 kc) and the resistive hybrid-π is valid.

4.4 NOISE PERFORMANCE OF COMMON-EMITTER AMPLIFIERS

In noise analysis of transistor amplifiers we are concerned with the relation between the power associated with the noise sources and the power available from the signal source. In this section we shall represent the noise performance by a parameter called the "noise temperature," which can be calculated on the basis of the noise models derived in the preceding section. The "noise temperature" is directly related to another commonly used parameter F, the "noise figure," which we shall discuss briefly later on.

4.4.1 *Noise Temperature*

Figure 4.5a shows a noisy amplifier connected to the Thévenin representation of a source. The voltage v_s represents the desired signal which we wish to reproduce amplified at the amplifier output. The resistance R_s is the Thévenin equivalent resistance of the

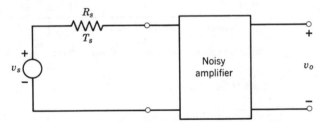

(a) Amplifier connected to Thévenin representation of source

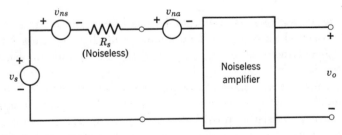

(b) Circuit with all noise referred to the input

Fig. 4.5. Thévenin representation of amplifier noise.

source, that is, the value of R_s is obtained on the basis of standard impedance considerations.

Inevitably there will be some noise associated with the source; for example, if the source is an electromagnetic pickup coil, there will be noise associated with the winding resistance of the coil. We choose to describe the source noise by associating a temperature T_s with the source resistance R_s. That is, we define a *source noise temperature* T_s which is related to the spectral density of the open-circuit voltage of the source by

$$T_s(f) \equiv S_v(f)/4kR_s \qquad (4.32a)$$

In the case of the pickup coil, the source noise temperature T_s might be very nearly equal to the ambient temperature of the source, but that is by no means necessary or even the usual case. For example, an antenna on a satellite might have an effective noise temperature of a few degrees Kelvin, even though the antenna might be quite a bit hotter. In addition, the noise temperature can be a function of frequency, as we shall see in Sec. 4.5. In short, the noise temperature of a source is just a convenient parameter for describing the noise voltage or noise current associated with that source.

If the spectral density is flat over the frequency range of interest, then T_s will be independent of frequency and we can then define T_s in terms of the mean-square voltage from the source. That is, we define T_s such that the mean-square open-circuit voltage from the source, when measured with an instrument of bandwidth Δf, will be

$$\overline{v_{ns}^2} = 4kT_sR_s\,\Delta f \qquad (4.32b)$$

Noise temperature is a useful parameter because it cannot be altered by means of an ideal transformer. For example, if a resistor is viewed through an ideal transformer of turns ratio n, the noise voltage will also be multiplied by n, but the noise temperature will remain unchanged (see Problem P4.3).

In addition to the source noise, there will always be some noise associated with the amplifier. A convenient way of specifying the amplifier noise is to define an *amplifier noise temperature* T_a as *that temperature which, if added to T_s, would make the noise from the source resistance R_s alone completely account for all noise in the* *amplifier and the source.* To illustrate this idea, assume for simplicity that the amplifier voltage gain, defined as $A_v = V_o/V_s$, is frequency-independent and that the mean-square value of the total output voltage (again measured with a meter of bandwidth Δf) is $\overline{v_o^2}$. If we further assume that the amplifier noise is not correlated with the source noise, as is almost always the case, we can express the mean-square output voltage as follows:

$$\overline{v_o^2} = \overline{[A_v(v_s - v_{ns} - v_{na})]^2} = A_v^2\overline{v_s^2} + A_v^2\overline{v_{ns}^2} + A_v^2\overline{v_{na}^2} \qquad (4.33)$$

Here $\overline{v_s^2}$ is the mean-square signal voltage; $\overline{v_{ns}^2}$ is the mean-square noise voltage of the source; and $\overline{v_{na}^2}$ is the mean-square noise from the amplifier, expressed as an *equivalent input noise* voltage as shown in Fig. 4.5b. Clearly we can find a single noise voltage v_e at the input, in series with R_s, such that we achieve the same noise at the output of the amplifier as that due to the source noise and the noise within the amplifier. On this basis Eq. 4.33 becomes

$$\overline{v_o^2} = A_v^2[\overline{v_s^2} + \overline{v_e^2}] \qquad (4.34a)$$

If, now, we associate the noise voltage v_e with the source resistance R_s by defining a new temperature $T_s + T_a$ for the resistor R_s, such that resistor R_s *alone* accounts for all of the noise in the system, then Eq. 4.34a becomes

$$\overline{v_o^2} = A_v^2[\overline{v_s^2} + 4k(T_s + T_a)R_s\,\Delta f] \qquad (4.34b)$$

(assuming that the source noise has a flat spectrum, and hence T_s is independent of frequency). The temperature T_a is, by definition, the amplifier noise temperature. Clearly T_a may be a function of many parameters including, particularly, the source resistance R_s, the operating points of all the transistors, and the temperatures of the amplifier components. Remember that T_a is a *fictitious* temperature and may be considerably less, or more, than the actual temperature of the amplifier.

It is important to note that we can derive the amplifier noise temperature equally well in terms of the amplifier short-circuit output current instead of the open-circuit voltage. The result would be the same, because the noise temperature indicates the *relative* strength of amplifier noise and source noise. In fact, we can consider the amplifier loaded arbitrarily without altering the result, as long as the same load is used for all output calculations. Equally important is the fact that T_a can be found with greater ease by assuming that $v_s = 0$ and $T_s = 0$, *provided only that there is no correlation among the sources* v_s, v_{ns}, and v_{na}.

The ideal for a low-noise amplifier is to have T_a much smaller than T_s. Usually, however, low noise is not the only important amplifier characteristic, and one must often strike a compromise between low noise and, for example, large bandwidth. Moreover, there are limits on how low T_a can be, even if we use the best possible transistors and circuits. The rest of this section is concerned with the calculation and minimization of noise temperature.

4.4.2 *Noise Minimization for* $r_x = 0$

For transistors operating at low current levels, shot noise is usually the most important noise. Thus, as a start, let us consider the amplifier model shown in Fig. 4.6. We assume that the frequency is low enough so that the resistive hybrid-π model applies, and that we can neglect r_x and r_μ. Also, it is assumed that frequencies are high enough so that $1/f$ noise is negligible.

For this model, it is simplest to calculate the mean-square short-circuit current within a bandwidth Δf. Also, we assume for this calculation that $v_s = 0$, and $T_s = 0$ so that $v_{ns} = 0$. On this basis, $\overline{i_o^2}$ becomes

$$\overline{i_o^2} = \overline{[i_{ni}g_m(r_\pi\|R_s) - i_{no}]^2} \tag{4.35a}$$

$$= \left(\frac{g_m r_\pi}{r_\pi + R_s}\right)^2 \left[\overline{i_{ni}^2}\,R_s^2 + \overline{i_{no}^2}\left(\frac{r_\pi + R_s}{g_m r_\pi}\right)^2\right] \tag{4.35b}$$

assuming the sources to be uncorrelated. Equation 4.35b has been written so that the mean-square voltages inside the brackets now have the significance of voltages "referred to the amplifier input."

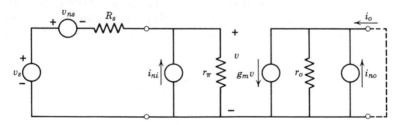

Fig. 4.6. Noise model of common-emitter amplifier, assuming $r_x = 0$, $r_\mu = \infty$, $f \cong 10$ kc.

Thus, on the basis of Eq. 4.34b, the amplifier noise temperature is given by

$$4kT_aR_s\,\Delta f = \overline{i_{ni}^2}\,R_s{}^2 + \overline{i_{no}^2}\left(\frac{r_\pi + R_s}{g_m r_\pi}\right)^2$$

Substituting for the mean-square values from Eqs. 4.29 and 4.30, we obtain

$$4kT_aR_s = 2qI_B{}'R_s{}^2 + 2q|I_C|\left(\frac{r_\pi + R_s}{g_m r_\pi}\right)^2 \qquad (4.36a)$$

or

$$\frac{T_a}{T} = \frac{q\,I_B{}'\,R_s}{2kT} + \frac{q|I_C|R_s}{2kTg_m{}^2}\left(\frac{1}{r_\pi} + \frac{1}{R_s}\right)^2 \qquad (4.36b)$$

where T is the actual temperature of the transistor. For convenience, we can express $I_B{}'$ and $|I_C|$ in terms of g_m, h'_{FE}, and β_0 defined as follows:

$$g_m \equiv \frac{|I_C|}{kT/q}\,; \qquad h'_{FE} \equiv \frac{|I_C|}{I_B{}'}\,; \qquad \beta_0 \equiv g_m r_\pi \qquad (4.37)$$

Thus we have:

$$\frac{T_a}{T} \cong \frac{g_m R_s}{2h'_{FE}} + \frac{1}{2g_m R_s} + \frac{1}{\beta_0} + \frac{g_m \cancel{R_s}}{\cancel{2}\beta_0{}^2} \qquad (4.38)$$

The last term in Eq. 4.38 can be neglected in comparison with the first term, because $\beta_0{}^2$ is almost always much greater than h'_{FE}. Notice that there is a definite distinction between h'_{FE} and β_0; one is the ratio of two direct currents (and $I_B{}'$ is not even the actual base current I_B), while the other is the incremental current gain.

From Eq. 4.38 we see that for either very small or very large values of R_s, T_a will be large, and that T_a has a minimum with respect to variations of R_s. In order to achieve this minimum, we must use a value of source resistance $R_{s(opt)}$; such that $(\partial T_a/\partial R_s) = 0$. Thus

$$\frac{\partial T_a}{\partial R_s} = T\left[\frac{g_m}{2h'_{FE}} - \frac{1}{2g_m R_s{}^2}\right] = 0$$

Therefore

$$R^2_{s(opt)} = \frac{h'_{FE}}{g_m{}^2} \qquad (4.39)$$

and the corresponding minimum noise temperature is given by

$$\frac{T_{a(\min)}}{T} = \sqrt{\frac{1}{h'_{FE}} + \frac{1}{\beta_0}} \cong \sqrt{\frac{1}{h'_{FE}}} \qquad (4.40)$$

As a specific example, suppose that we use a germanium transistor operating at $I_C = -100$ μa, $I_B = -0.5$ μa and $T = 290°K$. Suppose, further, that $I_3 + I_4$ in Eq. 4.31a (the base current with both junctions back-biased) is 0.25 μa. We then have $h'_{FE} = 100/(0.5 + 0.5) = 100$, so $T_{a(\min)} = 29°K$. In order to achieve this minimum value of T_a we must use $R^2_{s(\text{opt})} = 100/(0.004)^2$ or $R_{s(\text{opt})} = 2500$ ohms. The effect of neglecting the $1/\beta_0$ term in Eq. 4.40 amounts to only about a 3°K error, while neglecting the last term in Eq. 4.38 causes less than a 0.2°K error.

A reconsideration of the approximations in Eqs. 4.38 and 4.40 reveals that they are equivalent to assuming $r_\pi = \infty$. The reason that we can neglect the effect of r_π in such noise calculations can be seen from Eq. 4.36b. For R_s small, the collector-current shot noise term in the noise temperature expression becomes dominant and independent of r_π. For R_s large, the noise temperature expression is dominated by the base-current shot noise term, which again is independent of r_π.

We might conclude from Eq. 4.40 that the only important consideration for minimum noise was to achieve large values of h'_{FE}. Thus we might be tempted to increase the collector current to the point where h'_{FE} reaches a maximum. If we were to do this, however, the required source resistance would probably be very low, almost certainly less than the base resistance, which we have neglected. Thus, the preceding analysis does *not* lead us to the proper choice of *operating point* for minimum noise. We can, however, get some idea of the best transistor temperature T. For example, in the case of a germanium *pnp* transistor, h'_{FE} will not increase very rapidly with temperature. In fact, at low currents the effect of thermal generation of carriers may actually cause h'_{FE} to increase with decreasing temperature. Thus the transistor will usually give the lowest noise temperature T_a when the actual transistor temperature T is below normal room temperature.

In the case of a silicon *npn* transistor, $h'_{FE} \cong h_{FE}$, and typically h_{FE} will increase on the order of 1% per degree Kelvin. Thus

$T/\sqrt{h_{FE}}$ will actually decrease with increasing temperature; thus higher T, in this case, means lower T_a. At sufficiently elevated temperatures the thermal generation of carriers will, of course, become important; for silicon, there is usually an optimum transistor temperature somewhat above normal room temperature.

Since h'_{FE} is not a very rapid function of either operating point or temperature, it is clear that the primary prerequisite for low noise operation is a transistor with a large dc current gain h_{FE} and small I_{CO} and I_{EO}. Fortunately it is possible to build silicon transistors with values of h_{FE} in the vicinity of 500, and hence very good noise performance is possible. The really difficult problems are to achieve low noise for frequencies below about 1000 cps, where $1/f$ noise is troublesome, or at high impedance levels (on the order of $R_s > 1$ megohm) where Eq. 4.39 demands very low values of I_C, with a corresponding reduction in h'_{FE} and increase of $T_{a(\min)}$. In these situations the field-effect transistor has decided advantages for low noise operation.

4.4.3 *Optimum Bias for Minimum Noise*

To find the optimum bias for minimum noise in a transistor, we must include the base resistance and its associated noise generator. On the basis of Sec. 4.3.2, the noise model including r_x for the common-emitter amplifier appears as in Fig. 4.7a. It is clear that according to this model, the results of Sec. 4.4.2 can be modified by making two additions. Specifically, r_x must be added to R_s; and v_{nx} must be added to v_{ns} in a mean-square sense.

However, rather than duplicating the previous derivation, we shall follow a somewhat different path in order to illustrate an alternate approach to noise temperature calculations. We eventually want to refer all noise calculations to the input of the amplifier, so with that in mind we calculate the Thévenin source facing the resistor r_π, with the sources v_s and v_{ns} set to zero. In fact, we only need the Thévenin open-circuit voltage:

$$v_{i1} = v_{nx} + i_{ni}(R_s + r_x)$$

The output noise source can also be referred to the input by noting that an equivalent input source v_{i2} in series with R_s in Fig. 4.7a would produce a short-circuit current i_o equal to

$$i_o = v_{i2} \left(\frac{g_m r_\pi}{r_x + r_\pi + R_s} \right)$$

Thus, v_{i2} will cause the same output as i_{no} if

$$v_{i2} = i_{no} \left[\frac{r_x + r_\pi + R_s}{g_m r_\pi} \right]$$

To find the noise temperature, we equate the mean-square voltage from the source resistor R_s at a temperature T_a to the mean-square value of $v_{i1} + v_{i2}$. If all sources are uncorrelated,

$$4kT_a R_s \,\Delta f = \overline{v_{nx}^2} + \overline{i_{ni}^2}(R_s + r_x)^2 + \overline{i_{no}^2} \left(\frac{r_x + r_\pi + R_s}{g_m r_\pi} \right)^2 \qquad (4.41)$$

Identifying the mean-square values in terms of the dc currents, we obtain

$$4kT_a R_s = 2qI_B'(R_s + r_x)^2$$
$$+ 2q \,|I_C| \left(\frac{r_x + r_\pi + R_s}{g_m r_\pi} \right)^2 + 4kT r_x \qquad (4.42)$$

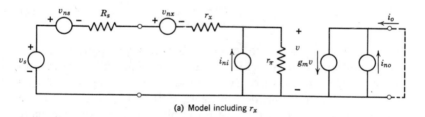

(a) Model including r_x

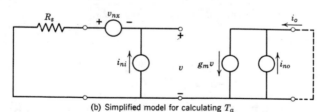

(b) Simplified model for calculating T_a

Fig. 4.7. Noise models for common-emitter amplifier, assuming $r_\mu = \infty$, $f \cong 10$ kc.

If we assume that $r_x \ll r_\pi$ and $r_x \ll R_s$, then Eq. 4.42 is very similar to Eq. 4.36a, except for the additional term resulting from the noise in r_x. Thus, by analogy with Eq. 4.38, and neglecting as before terms in β_o, we obtain

$$4kT_aR_s \cong 2qI_B{}'R_s{}^2 + 2q\,|I_C|\,g_m{}^{-2} + 4kTr_x \qquad (4.43)$$

$$\frac{T_a}{T} \cong \frac{g_mR_s}{2h'_{FE}} + \frac{1}{2g_mR_s} + \frac{r_x}{R_s} \qquad (4.44)$$

A closer examination of Eqs. 4.42 and 4.43 shows that in forming Eq. 4.43 we are, in effect, neglecting the resistor r_x itself, but taking into account the noise it produces. Equations 4.43 and 4.44 can therefore be calculated directly from the simplified model of Fig. 4.7b.

It is not difficult to show from Eq. 4.44 that the minimum value of T_a with respect to variations in R_s is

$$\frac{T_{a(\min)}}{T} \cong \sqrt{\frac{1 + 2g_mr_x}{h'_{FE}}} \qquad (4.45)$$

and the corresponding optimum value for R_s is given by

$$R^2_{s(\text{opt})} = \frac{h'_{FE}}{g_m{}^2}\,[1 + 2g_mr_x] \qquad (4.46)$$

We are now in a position to estimate the optimum operating point. As the collector current is increased, at first h'_{FE} will increase and hence $T_{a(\min)}$ will decrease. Eventually, however, the $(1 + 2g_mr_x)$ term will increase faster, percentagewise, than h'_{FE} so an optimum collector current will exist. Thus, for minimum noise, we must have

$$\frac{1}{1 + 2g_mr_x}\,\frac{\partial 2g_mr_x}{\partial I_C}\bigg|_{V_{CE}} = \frac{1}{h'_{FE}}\,\frac{\partial h'_{FE}}{\partial I_C}\bigg|_{V_{CE}} \qquad (4.47)$$

From Eq. 4.47, we have

$$\frac{2g_mr_x}{1 + 2g_mr_x} = \frac{I_C}{h'_{FE}}\,\frac{\partial h'_{FE}}{\partial I_C}\bigg|_{V_{CE}} \qquad (4.48)$$

We can use Eq. 4.48 provided we know how h'_{FE} varies with I_C. This could be done on the basis of measured data, but in the case of a silicon transistor, for which $h'_{FE} \cong h_{FE}$, we can use a simple approximation. Typically the collector and base currents are given by expressions of the form:

$$I_C = I_{CK} e^{qV_{EB}/kT}$$
$$I_B = I_{BK} e^{qV_{BE}/nkT} \tag{4.49}$$

In Eqs. 4.49 the signs correspond to an *npn* unit, and I_{CK}, I_{BK}, and n are constants. Typically, n is on the order of 1.2 and is readily measured, since $r_\pi = \partial V_{BE}/\partial I_B = nI_B/(kT/q)$. Thus

$$\beta_0 = g_m r_\pi = nh_{FE}$$

$$n = \frac{\beta_0}{h_{FE}} \tag{4.50}$$

That is, n is the ratio of the incremental gain β_0 to the dc gain h_{FE}.
Using Eqs. 4.49, we have

$$h_{FE} = \frac{I_{CK}^{1/n}}{I_{BK}} I_C^{(1-1/n)}$$

$$\left. \frac{\partial h_{FE}}{\partial I_C} \right|_{V_{CE}} = \frac{n-1}{nI_B} \tag{4.51}$$

And, thus, for the optimum bias conditions, we must have

$$\frac{2g_m r_x}{1 + 2g_m r_x} = \frac{n-1}{n}$$

or

$$1 + 2g_m r_x = n \tag{4.52}$$

The minimum noise temperature is then

$$\frac{T_{a(min)}}{T} = \sqrt{\frac{n}{h_{FE}}}$$

and the corresponding value of R_s is given by

$$R_{s(opt)}^2 = \frac{nh_{FE}}{g_m^2} = \frac{\beta_0}{g_m^2} = \frac{r_\pi}{g_m} \tag{4.53}$$

As a specific numerical example, assume that a silicon transistor has $n = \beta_0/h_{FE} = 1.2$, and $r_x = 500$ ohms for low values of collector current. Thus the proper operating point, based on Eq. 4.52, requires

$$1 + 2g_m r_x = 1.2$$

$$\frac{1}{g_m} = 10r_x = 5000 \ \Omega$$

If the transistor is at a temperature of 290°K, the above condition is equivalent to specifying $I_C = 5\mu a$ as the dc collector bias current. If we further assume that $h_{FE} = 120$ at $I_C = 5\mu a$, then, from Eq. 4.53,

$$T_{a(\min)} = (290°K) \sqrt{\frac{1.2}{120}} = 29°K$$

and the optimum source resistance is

$$R_{s(\text{opt})} = 5000 \ \sqrt{1.2 \times 120} = 60 \ \text{kilohms}.$$

Note that our assumptions that $r_x \ll R_s$ and $r_x \ll r_\pi$ are clearly justified.

The actual noise contributed by r_x is, typically, only about 10% of the total noise if I_C and R_s are adjusted for minimum T_a. However, if r_x can be decreased, then the optimum I_C is increased and thus h_{FE}' will be increased and a lower noise temperature is realized. Also, if it is unavoidable to have a low R_s, then Eq. 4.44 indicates that $T_a/T > r_x/R_s$. Hence a low r_x is clearly desirable.

4.4.5 *Graphical Representation of Noise Performance*

The preceding discussion has made it clear that, for a given transistor, the most important circuit variables for noise calculations are R_s and $|I_C|$. Thus a convenient means of representing noise performance graphically is to plot contours of constant noise temperature in the $|I_C|$ versus R_s plane. Such plots are commonly given by manufacturers and afford a simple basis for circuit design. Figure 4.8 shows such a plot for a typical silicon planar transistor.

For comparison with the experimental data, Fig. 4.9 shows theoretical contours based on the model of Fig. 4.4a, assuming h_{FE}' is independent of current. These curves do not indicate an optimum operating point because the current dependence of h_{FE}' has not been included. Otherwise, however, they show a close resem-

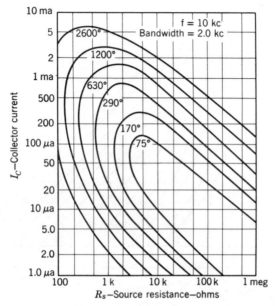

Fig. 4.8. Experimentally determined contours of constant noise temperature in °K for an amplifier using an *npn* silicon transistor. $T = 25°C$, $V_{CE} = 5$ volts.

blance to the measured curves. In fact, one of the best ways to deduce the effective value of r_x is to interrelate these theoretical and experimental curves.

The dotted and dashed lines in Fig. 4.9 are used to separate the plot into three regions. Roughly speaking, within each region one noise source has dominant importance, and is so indicated. For instance, with large R_s and large $|I_C|$, the shot noise associated with I_B is the most important noise. Note that the dotted and dashed lines represent a kind of optimum condition. If R_s is specified, then the optimum bias is given by the intersection of the dashed line with the appropriate R_s line, while if the bias current is specified, the optimum source resistance is given by the intersection with the dotted line.

According to both theoretical and experimental curves, good noise performance can be achieved over quite a wide range of source resistance and bias, provided that R_s is relatively large compared with r_x, and the source resistance and bias are "matched"

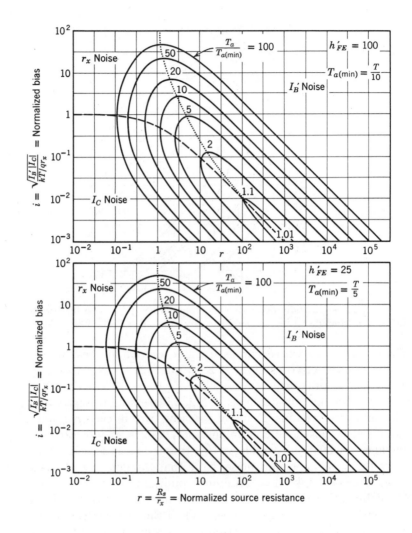

Fig. 4.9. Theoretical contours of constant noise temperature for a common-emitter amplifier at temperature T. Plotted curves correspond to

$$\frac{T_a}{T_{a(\min)}} = \left[\frac{1}{2ri} + \frac{ri}{2} + i + \frac{i}{2r}\right] + \frac{(h_{FE})^{1/2}}{r}; \quad T_{a(\min)} = \left[h'_{FE}\right]^{-1/2} T.$$

to each other. That is, according to Eq. 4.53 we should insure that

$$R_s \cong \sqrt{r_\pi / g_m} \qquad (4.54)$$

Remember that Eq. 4.54 represents a match in a noise sense only. Choosing R_s for best (lowest) noise temperature does not usually coincide with a choice based on maximum power-gain considerations. Moreover, the adjustment of R_s for best noise performance can only be done by proper choice of bias current, use of a transformer, or the equivalent: the use of a resistor in series or shunt with the source can *never* effect any improvement in noise performance.

The preceding derivations have all been based on a single-stage amplifier. When additional stages are cascaded, the noise temperature will increase somewhat because of noise sources associated with the added stages. In order to minimize the increase in noise it is desirable to achieve large gains in the first stage and use a moderately low-noise second stage. Thus, for example, if transformerless interstage coupling is used, the dc base current for the second stage should be significantly less than the dc collector current for the first stage. Note that if the noise optimization had led to a mode of operation which produced very little power gain, then the noise temperature of a single stage would no longer afford a reasonable measure of transistor noise. For example, connecting a short circuit between base and collector and operating with $I_B = I_C = 0$ will produce a noise temperature essentially equal to zero. However, this could hardly be construed as an optimum design. Fortunately, for most transistors in the normal bias region, the conditions for minimum noise temperature coincide with conditions for reasonable power gain, so the noise temperature of the input stage is a good measure of noise performance of the entire amplifier.

Although this chapter has been based on a common-emitter example, the same methods are applicable to other configurations. Usually the minimum noise temperature is practically independent of whether a common-emitter, common-base, or common-collector configuration is used. However, the common-emitter input stage is usually used because it is capable of greater power gain, and thus noise in the second stage is minimized.

4.4.6 *Noise Figure and Noise Resistance*

The "spot noise figure," designated F, is an alternative and commonly used parameter for specifying noise performance. For two-port networks, the spot noise figure is directly related to noise temperature by the relation:

$$F \equiv 1 + \frac{T_a}{290°\text{K}} \qquad (4.55)$$

An alternative, and equivalent, definition is: *F is the ratio of noise power delivered by the amplifier to a load, to noise power that would be delivered if the only noisy component were the source resistance, R_s, at a standard temperature of 290°K.* Thus, we see that $F = 1$ implies that the amplifier itself contributes no noise, and for any practical amplifier we *must* have $F > 1$. Typically, F is given in decibels, so, for example, a noise temperature of 29°K implies $F = 1.1$ or $F = 0.4$ db.

Historically, the noise figure was once the most commonly used noise measure. However, it has also been commonly misused, primarily because of lack of precision in some of its early definitions, and improper understanding of the role of the 290°K reference temperature.

The noise performance of a two-port network can also be specified in terms of a "noise resistance," R_n, defined by

$$\frac{R_n}{R_s} = \frac{T_a}{290°\text{K}} \qquad (4.56)$$

The parameter R_n can also be defined as *that resistance which, at 290°K, has a Thévenin equivalent noise source equal to the equivalent amplifier input noise voltage.* Note that R_n depends on R_s. The noise resistance is, of course, a different function of R_s than is either F or T_a; so minimizing R_n with respect to R_s is not equivalent to minimizing either F or T_a with respect to R_s.

Notice that a specification of R_s and T_a is equivalent to a specification of R_n and F. For most purposes, however, the former is less confusing, and can be more readily extended to multi-input systems.

4.5 NOISE CALCULATIONS IN FREQUENCY-DEPENDENT NETWORKS

Except for the derivations of Johnson and shot noise, all of the calculations in the preceding sections of this chapter have been carried out in the time domain. This procedure is valid because we have, thus far, assumed all networks to be resistive over the frequency range of interest. In this section we discuss methods of calculating noise performance over a broader frequency range, such that the frequency-dependence of the networks must be accounted for. The discussion must now be phrased in terms of frequency-domain quantities and, in the light of Section 4.1.3, the essential problem will be to relate the output spectral density to the input spectral density.

4.5.1 *Calculations of Output Spectral Density with One Noise Source Input*

The derivation of the expression for the output spectral density of a network is based on the autocorrelations of the input and output voltages v_i and v_o (Fig. 4.10).

$$R_i(\tau) = \lim_{T \to \infty} \frac{1}{2T} \int_{-T}^{T} v_i(t) v_i(t + \tau) \, dt \tag{4.57}$$

$$R_o(\tau) = \lim_{T \to \infty} \frac{1}{2T} \int_{-T}^{T} v_o(t) v_o(t + \tau) \, dt \tag{4.58}$$

In addition, we need the convolution integral, which relates $v_o(t)$ to $v_i(t)$ through the impulse response:

$$v_o(t) = \int_{-\infty}^{\infty} h(t_1) v_i(t - t_1) \, dt_1 \tag{4.59}$$

$$\equiv h(t) \, \textcircled{X} \, v_i(t)$$

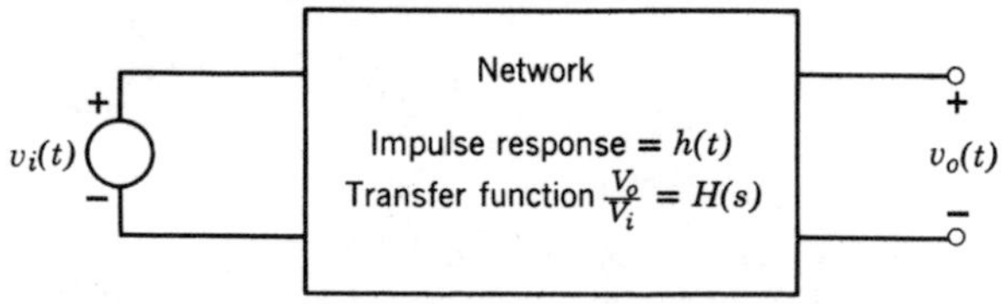

Fig. 4.10. Definition of variables.

where the symbol X indicates the operation of convolution. If Eq. 4.59 is used to eliminate v_o from Eq. 4.58, and suitable changes of variable and changes of order of integration are made,* we find

$$R_o(\tau) = R_i(\tau) \ X \ R_h(\tau) \tag{4.60}$$

where R_h is the autocorrelation of the impulse response:

$$R_h(\tau) = \int_{-\infty}^{\infty} h(t)h(t+\tau)\, dt \tag{4.61}$$

Because convolution in the time domain corresponds to multiplication in the frequency domain, we find, on transforming Eq. 4.60 into the frequency domain and changing to one-sided spectra,

$$S_{v(\text{output})} = S_{v(\text{input})}\, |H(f)|^2 \tag{4.62}$$

That is, the *output spectral density can be found by multiplying the input spectral density by the squared magnitude of the transfer function.*

To illustrate, let us calculate the output noise spectral density for the simple RC network shown in Fig. 4.11*a*. The circuit model in Fig. 4.11*b* explicitly shows the noise source due to the resistor. Also, the signal source has been set to zero. The input spectral density of the noise source v_{nr} is, from Secs. 4.2.2 and 4.2.3,

$$S_{v(\text{input})} = 4kTR$$

The desired transfer function for this problem is the voltage ratio

$$\frac{V_o(s)}{V_i(s)} = H(s) = \frac{1}{RCs + 1}$$

Thus, from Eq. 4.62,

$$S_{v(\text{output})} = \frac{4kTR}{(2\pi RCf)^2 + 1}$$

---

* See, for example, W. B. Davenport and W. L. Root, loc. cit., p. 182, or S. J. Mason and H. J. Zimmermann, *Electronic Circuits, Signals and Systems*, Wiley, New York, 1960, p. 344.

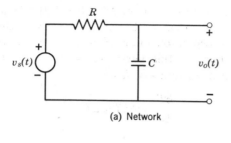

(a) Network

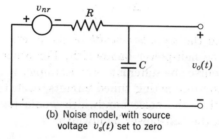

(b) Noise model, with source
voltage $v_s(t)$ set to zero

Fig. 4.11. Noise calculations in a simple RC network.

To find the mean-square value of the output voltage v_o, we use Parseval's theorem (Eq. 4.9).

$$\overline{v_o{}^2(t)} = \int_0^\infty S_{v(\text{output})}\, df$$

$$= 4kT \int_0^\infty \frac{R}{(2\pi RCf)^2 + 1}\, df$$

On the basis that the definite integral

$$\int_0^\infty \frac{a}{a^2 + x^2}\, dx = \frac{\pi}{2} \qquad \text{for} \quad a > 0$$

we find that the mean-square value of the output noise voltage of a simple RC filter is

$$\overline{v_o{}^2(t)} = \frac{kT}{C}$$

4.5.2 *Noise Bandwidth*

By the usual definition, the half-power bandwidth of the filter in the preceding example is $f_h = 1/(2\pi RC)$. Clearly this is *not* the appropriate value to substitute for Δf in Eq. 4.21 to find the mean-square output noise, because the bandwidth Δf in that equation was based on a sharp-cutoff filter. However, by equating the two results, we can find for this particular single-pole RC filter, the required value of Δf in terms of R and C.

$$\frac{kT}{C} = 4kTR\,\Delta f$$

$$\therefore \Delta f = \frac{1}{4RC}$$

This is called the *noise bandwidth* of the filter, and in this case is $\pi/2$ times the half-power bandwidth. For other filters the result would, of course, be different. For example, if a tuned amplifier had three non-interacting tuned circuits, each tuned to the same frequency, then the noise bandwidth would have been only 5% greater than the half-power bandwidth.

4.5.3 Calculation of Output Spectral Density for Several Noise Source Inputs

If we wish to find the output spectral density for a network with more than one noise source, some modification of Eq. 4.62 is required. Suppose we have n noise sources, with voltages $v_1, v_2, v_3 \ldots$ Then, by superposition,

$$v_o(t) = [h_1(t) \otimes v_1(t)] + [h_2(t) \otimes v_2(t)] + \cdots \qquad (4.63)$$

where $h_k(t)$ is the response at the output terminals to an impulse applied at the kth input. Following the same procedure as before, that is, substituting Eq. 4.63 into Eq. 4.58 and taking the Fourier transform of the resulting equation, we obtain

$$W_o(f) = W_1(f)\,|H_1(f)|^2 + W_2(f)\,|H_2(f)|^2 + \cdots$$
$$+ W_{12}(f)H_1(f)H_2{}^*(f) + W_{21}(f)H_1{}^*(f)H_2(f) + \cdots \qquad (4.64)$$

where $W_{12}(f)$ is the cross-spectral density of the noise sources v_1 and v_2, defined as the Fourier transform of their cross-correlation function $R_{12}(\tau)$

$$R_{12}(\tau) = \lim_{T \to \infty} \frac{1}{2T} \int_{-T}^{T} v_1(t)v_2(t + \tau)\,d\tau \qquad (4.65)$$

Thus this term exists only if there is correlation between these two noise sources.

To convert from the two-sided $W(f)$ to the one-sided $S(f)$ spectral representation, we note from Eq. 4.65 that $R_{12}(\tau)$ and $R_{21}(\tau)$ are real although not in general even, and that

$$R_{12}(\tau) = R_{21}(-\tau) \tag{4.66}$$

Because W_{12}, W_{21}, H_1, and H_2 are all transforms of real functions, each of these functions and any products will be such that the real part is even and the imaginary part is odd. It follows that because of Eq. 4.66

$$W_{21}(f) = W_{12}^*(f) = W_{12}(-f) \tag{4.67}$$

Hence the term containing W_{12} in Eq. 4.64 is the complex conjugate of the term containing W_{21}, and thus

$$W_{12}(f)H_1(f)H_2^*(f) + W_{21}(f)H_1^*(f)H_2(f)$$
$$= 2 \, \text{Re}[W_{12}(f)H_1(f)H_2^*(f)] \tag{4.68}$$

and the "real part" is an *even* function of f. Thus Eq. 4.64 can be written as a sum of terms which are even in f, and hence we can readily convert to single-sided spectra:

$$S_o(f) = S_1(f) \, |H_1(f)|^2 + S_2(f) \, |H_2(f)|^2 + \dots$$
$$+ 2 \, \text{Re} \, [S_{12}(f)H_1(f)H_2^*(f)] + \dots \tag{4.69}$$

where

$$S_{12}(f) = 2W_{12}(f) \qquad \text{for} \quad f \geq 0$$

To illustrate the use of Eq. 4.69, let us calculate the output noise spectral density of a single-stage transistor amplifier, ignoring for simplicity r_x and its associated noise (i.e., the same calculation as in Sec. 4.4.2, except this time with C_π and $C\mu$ included in the computation). The noise model for this amplifier is shown in Fig. 4.12. We know the spectral densities of v_{ns}, i_{ni}, and i_{no} from previous calculations. Assume the sources are uncorrelated so that the cross-spectral densities $S_{jk}(f)$ are all zero (an accurate assumption for $f < f_T/2$). To calculate the spectral density of the short-circuit output noise current, $S'_{i(\text{output})}$, we set v_s to zero, and convert the source resistance and its noise source to the Norton equivalent. Then the required transfer function from input to output is

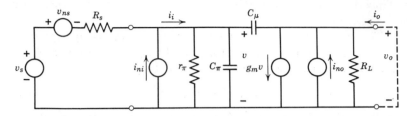

Fig. 4.12. Transistor noise calculation including the effect of C_μ and C_π.

$$\frac{I_o(s)}{I_i(s)} = A_i(s) \cong \frac{g_m}{g_\pi + G_s + s[C_\pi + C_\mu]} \qquad (4.70)$$

For the output noise source, the desired transfer function is obviously unity. From Eqs. 4.69, 4.27, and 4.28, we find the output spectral density to be

$$S'_{i(\text{output})} = [2qI_B' + 4kT_sG_s] |A_i|^2 + [2q |I_C|] \qquad (4.71)$$

4.5.4 *Frequency Dependence of Noise Temperature*

One interpretation of Eq. 4.71 is that when C_π and C_μ are included in transistor noise calculations, the noise temperature of the amplifier becomes a function of frequency. To show this, we again find the required temperature of the source resistor *alone* which would give the same output noise spectral density as that calculated above.

$$S'_{i(\text{output})} = 4k(T_s + T_a)G_s |A_i|^2 \qquad (4.72)$$

Equating this result to that obtained in Eq. 4.71 and eliminating T_s, we find

$$4kT_aG_s = 2qI_B' + \frac{2q |I_C|}{|A_i|^2} \qquad (4.73)$$

Substituting from Eq. 4.70 for A_i, we obtain

$$4kT_aG_s = 2qI_B' + 2q |I_C| \frac{(G_s + g_\pi)^2 + \omega^2(C_\pi + C_\mu)^2}{g_m{}^2} \qquad (4.74)$$

Observe, again, that the noise temperature equation (Eq. 4.74), *does not contain the load resistor R_L*, because *noise temperature is independent of the load*, and thus can be calculated under arbitrary load conditions (see Problem P4.4.) Note, however, that *the output* *spectral density is a function of the load resistor,* because both power levels and bandwidths change as R_L is varied.

To complete the noise temperature calculation, we solve Eq. 4.74 for T_a and find, on substituting from Eq. 4.38,

$$\frac{T_a(\omega)}{T} \cong \frac{T_a(f = 10 \text{ kc})}{T} + \frac{\omega^2(C_\pi + C_\mu)^2}{2G_s g_m} \tag{4.75}$$

Because $\omega_T = g_m/(C_\pi + C_\mu)$, Eq. 4.75 can be rewritten as

$$\frac{T_a(f)}{T} \cong \frac{T_a(f = 10 \text{ kc})}{T} + \frac{g_m}{2G_s} \frac{f^2}{f_T^2} \tag{4.76}$$

For the special case where T_a at 10 kc is optimized, as in Sec. 4.4.2, Eq. 4.76 reduces to

$$\frac{T_a(f)}{T} \cong \sqrt{\frac{1}{h'_{FE}}} + \frac{\sqrt{h'_{FE}}}{2} \frac{f^2}{f_T^2} \tag{4.77}$$

for frequencies greater than a few kilocycles. Note that T_a will increase to about twice its minimum value for $f = \sqrt{2/h'_{FE}} f_T$, so it is important to use a transistor with f_T much greater than the upper half-power frequency of the amplifier. Note also that at high frequencies the first term in Eq. 4.77 is negligible, so it may be desirable to increase the bias current in order to increase f_T. Unfortunately, the high-frequency noise analysis is complicated by the bias-dependence and frequency-dependence of r_x, because r_x takes on a more important role in high-frequency amplifiers. However, we shall not consider this problem here.

For low frequencies, the noise power will vary approximately as $1/f$, so $T_a(f)$ will have the form:

$$\frac{T_a(f)}{T} = \frac{f_L}{f} + \frac{T_a(f = 10 \text{ kc})}{T} + \frac{g_m}{2G_s} \frac{f^2}{f_T^2} \tag{4.78}$$

where f_L is a measurable constant and depends on bias and source impedance. Figure 4.13 shows measured data for a typical low-noise amplifier, and it is seen to have roughly the frequency dependence indicated in Eq. 4.78, $f_l \approx 400$ cycles.

Another way to portray the frequency dependence of noise temperature is by means of a number of noise contour curves of the type shown in Fig. 4.8. Figure 4.14 shows such a set for the same transistor as in Fig. 4.13.

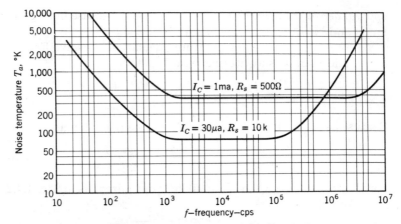

Fig. 4.13. Noise temperature versus frequency for a typical common-emitter amplifier. $V_{CE} = 5$ volts, $T = 25°C$.

It is important to note that, for low values of collector current, f_T will vary approximately as $|I_C|^{-1}$. At collector currents of a few microamperes, even the best transistors will not have f_T greater than about 1 mc, and thus the value of $T_{a(min)}$ will depend upon C_π and C_μ for frequencies not much, if any, above the audio band. For tuned, low-noise amplifiers operating in the range of several megacycles, the optimum operating point will depend quite strongly on the dependence of f_T on collector current. The methods discussed in this chapter can be used for analysing this high-frequency problem.

PROBLEMS

P4.1   The discussion leading up to Eq. 4.11a, made no mention of holes or electrons but, rather, was based on "current pulses." Does it matter whether the current pulses are made up mostly of holes, mostly of electrons, or equal amounts of holes and electrons? Explain.

P4.2   Show that the two noise models of Figs. 4.4a and 4.4b agree if:

$$r_x = r_B \frac{(n + 1)(2n + 1)}{6n^2}$$

P4.3   Show that an ideal transformer multiplies the mean-square noise voltage of a resistor by the square of the turns ratio, but that it leaves the noise temperature unchanged.

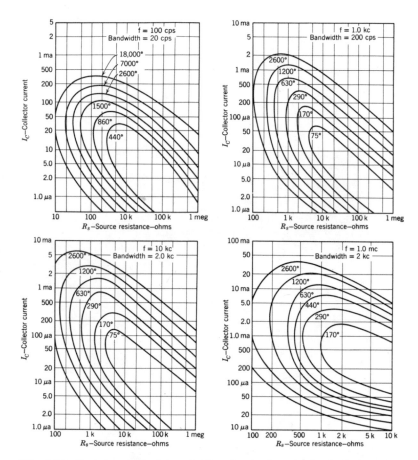

Fig. 4.14. Experimentally determined contours of constant noise temperature in °K for the same amplifier used in Fig. 4.13.

P4.4 Repeat the calculation of noise temperature for Fig. 4.12 (Sec. 4.5.4) except this time calculate in terms of the output voltage $V_o(s)$ across an arbitrary (nonzero) load R_L. Your answer should check with Eq. 4.74, thus confirming that the noise temperature is independent of the transistor load.

Index